PENGUIN BOOKS

A240

THE ANT WORLD

DEREK WRAGGE MORLEY

THE ANT WORLD

*

Derek Wragge Morley

PENGUIN BOOKS

Penguin Books Ltd, Harmondsworth, Middlesex

U.S.A.: Penguin Books Inc., 3300 Clipper Mill Road, Baltimore 11, Md
[*Educational Representative:*
D. C. Heath & Co., 285 Columbus Avenue, Boston 16, Mass]

CANADA: Penguin Books (Canada) Ltd, 47 Green Street,
Saint Lambert, Montreal, P.Q.

AUSTRALIA: Penguin Books Pty Ltd, 762 Whitehorse Road,
Mitcham, Victoria

SOUTH AFRICA: Penguin Books (S.A.) Pty Ltd, Gibraltar House,
Regents Road, Sea Point, Cape Town

—

First published 1953
Reprinted 1955

Made and printed in Great Britain
by Wyman & Sons Ltd
London, Reading, and Fakenham

CONTENTS

*

LIST OF ILLUSTRATIONS

*

CHAPTER I

The Popular Ant and the Real Ant

*

SOMETIMES on a really hot summer's day at the height of the mid-day sun, gently stirring masses of wood ants can be seen clustered on the sunny side of their hillock for an hour's siesta. But such a sight of lazing ants is exceptional. It is for their industry and their constant and often apparently aimless, bustling to and fro that the ants are renowned.

To the ancients, their restless activity seemed more purposeful, for many of the ants of the Middle East and the Southern Mediterranean shores collect stores of seeds for food, and could be seen carrying this recognized provender back to their nests. Indeed an ancient Jewish Mosaic Law, said to date back to the time of Solomon, states that the seed found in the nests of these harvesting ants must be given to the poor.

It was to these same ants, of the genera *Pheidole* and *Messor*, that Solomon referred when he bade the sluggard 'Go to the ant and be wise' (Proverbs vi. 6, 7, 8). These ants keep the seeds they collect in special chambers where, owing to the moistness of their surroundings, they soon start to germinate. When the first green sprout, or radicle, appears, the ants bite it off and at once bring the seeds out of the nest and place them in the sun to dry. During this drying process the starch in the seeds turns to sugar, giving the ants a convenient supply of attractive food.

It was their constant busyness in this obviously laudable activity of garnering in food and laying it in storage chambers within the nest that so intrigued and impressed writers like Pliny, who noted that they continued to work throughout the night in summer when the moon was at its fullest and brightest, and Aelian, who compared the complicated arrangement of galleries and chambers in their nests with the famous labyrinths of Crete and Greece. For centuries it was really believed that a species of ant 'not so large as a dog, but bigger than a fox' lived in the deserts of Arabia where it mined gold. Expeditions were even sent out to locate the ants and capture their gold – gold which was really only a parable about their industry which if copied would yield riches.

In the same way the ancient Greeks made this parable of the goodness of the ants' industry into a religious fable. One of the sons of Zeus, so the story goes, desired Eurymedusa, mother of the Graces, but wooed her without success as she was not deceived by his protestations of true affection. So in desperation he turned himself into an ant and she, being unable to refuse the protestations of this honest toiler, yielded herself to him. This son of Zeus became the king of the ants, and the progeny of the offspring of this liaison with Eurymedusa became the Myrmedones, a name coined from the first half of his new name of ant king (myrmex) and the second half of hers (medusa). The tale continues with a variety of histories of these offspring who eventually became the followers of Achilles, whence their reputation as fierce and utterly devoted and implacable followers gave us our present word of Myrmidon, and its meaning.

But St Jerome and also Solomon saw the ants in another light, as creatures of unusual societies in which all work together with none superior to another and where no individual has private property, but everything belongs to everyone. It was watching this communal life that, according to St Jerome, inspired the monk Malchus to return from the outside world to the communal life of the monastery, and which caused Solomon to wonder how their societies could be organized when they have 'no guide, overseer, or ruler.'

In those days there was no concept of complete equality of human individuals, and there were no machines, so the dangers of men becoming 'like the ants', machine-like, in an egalitarian state, could not be pointed out.

The Popular Ant and the Real Ant

Actually ants are no more industrious than most fairly active insects, or for that matter than most human beings, neither are they automatons. Both reputations are unjustified. Each individual ant spends several of its waking hours each day dozing or just grooming itself or a colleague. Of course, ants do not have the mental abilities to undertake leisure occupations at all similar to ours, but mutual grooming of one another, and to a lesser degree of themselves, does seem to provide them with something akin to pleasure or enjoyment. They also have mock battles and tussles one with another, exhibiting every sign of *joie de vivre*. If they doze, they may do so lying down, or they may remain, like a horse, standing up. When they lie down they either huddle together in groups in a chamber inside the nest, or else they find or scrape out a convenient individual hollow either inside or outside, in which to lay themselves. When sleeping lying down they fold up their legs and feelers, resting them flat against the body. In this state they are less easily awaked and often seem to wish to sleep again when disturbed. However, when they do awake, a very human-like ritual of stretching of limbs and mandibles (the large jaws) occurs, the latter looking every bit like a series of deep, then lesser, yawns; which it is not, because ants don't breathe through their mouths, but through holes in the sides of their bodies called spiracles. These spiracles, of which there are a pair to each segment of the body, lead to a vast system of branching tubes called the tracheae, which take the air to every part of the body. After the stretching a prolonged toilette follows before finally the ant is fully awake and ready once more to be its industrious-seeming self.

While the mental abilities of ants are limited – for example, they have no proper language, cannot be said to reason (to think things out), and do not, except in one case (see p. 157) use tools – their mental powers should not be underrated. They can learn the correct route in simple mazes which have six blind alleys, and individual ants vary in their ability to do this and in the speed (or number of runs through the maze) in which they learn their lesson. Just as

9

in the maze, so it is in the world of work; some individuals learn to do jobs better and more quickly than other ants in the nest.

These quicker learners are the primitive leaders of the colony, the 'excitement centres'. They are called 'excitement centres' because, although they determine what activities are carried out and when, they do not do so by sitting down and thinking about it and then giving directions to the other ants, but they excite the other ants into doing the different jobs by starting to do them themselves. The excitement centre ants are in effect the first individuals in each colony to respond to the stimulus of jobs needing to be done. The settling down to work of the twenty or thirty excitement centre ants soon arouses in the other ants feelings of their own hunger and need to go out foraging, or their own instincts to repair a broken part of the nest or to build new chambers to provide accommodation for a rapidly-expanding brood.

The jobs done by each ant will change when new stimuli come into play: for example, licking the grubs may change to going out to forage if they show signs of hunger or moving them to another chamber as the sun comes out and the temperature changes. Also as each job nears completion, or when the individual excitement centre ant has worked at it for a long time and is tiring, the drawing power which attracts other ants to the work and keeps them at it grows less. Workers will, as it were, be laid off and open to be attracted to other tasks, leaving the final completion of the nearly finished one to a few or even to a single individual.

The same system works within the different jobs, causing the attraction and counter-attraction of ants between all the various centres of activity. Within the different tasks also the learning of the individual ants plays its part. Some learn to forage at one spot and some at another – some near the nest and some farther away. While responding to the excitement of one of these ant 'leaders' to go out and forage, the other ant or ants may follow it to the same place. In this case the following ant may learn to go there also on future occasions, but often it will only follow the excitement centre ant into performing the operation of foraging and will then set about going to the district or particular spot where it has been most frequently.

Thus by attraction and counter-attraction the seemingly complex round of jobs of the ant community gets started, worked out, and usually fairly economically and successfully achieved. Food-getting is the most important task. It is no light one to get in food enough for from 40,000 to half a million individuals each day. A colony of 40,000 carnivorous ants will eat a quart of insect food (equivalent to over 20,000 insects) every day during the active summer months. Yet there are always several times more ants in the nest than there are out foraging. Inside the nest the queens must be carefully tended and guarded, and the eggs they lay carried off to the appropriate chamber. The brood require constant attention, for the larvae (grubs) must be fed and unceasingly licked, so that their skins are kept moist, and the cocoons must be watched so that ants ready to hatch out can be helped to emerge. Few ants can escape from their cocoons or pupal skins unaided. The nest structure also requires continual care and must be kept scrupulously clean, properly drained, and proof against enemy invasion. Then there are the aphid cows (greenflies, blackflies, and whiteflies), both inside and outside the nest, to be milked, or other guests to be tended or kept from prowling too near the queens or brood. For in each ants' nest there are many such insect guests, especially of the beetle kind. Some five thousand species of insects and spiders are found only in the nests of ants, living there permanently as either welcome or tolerated lodgers.

The feelers of ants with which they constantly touch one another are their noses. The tapping of feelers is not a matter of gossiping, but of recognizing friend or foe (for each individual of each colony has a special colony odour badge) and of friendly gesture or excited warning of work to be done or enemy at the gates. Although some species of ants can make sounds like a grasshopper by rubbing one part of the body against another (this is called stridulation, and the sounds produced are too high pitched and too weak for us to hear), there is no essential difference in the limitation of their language. For such stridulation only occurs when the individual is excited. It just says, in effect, 'I am excited over here', nothing more. Gesture and action is the limit of ant speech, and even that gesture doesn't include 'Come here and help me do this'. It is limited to 'Look here, I'm very busy doing this.' After that it is all a matter of not being able to stand by and let another chap do all the work. On very rare occasions this message may seem to change to a peremptory 'Come here and do this,' as when the excitement centre ant picks up another ant and bodily pulls it towards a spot where food has been found or other work is needed. But this is very rare indeed and plays little part in normal ant behaviour. The excitement centre ant is essentially a job spotter, passing on his having seen a job by doing it.

Only when the nest is moved to a new site are ants forcibly made to do something by other ants. Then those who won't move, or haven't woken up to the fact that a move is on, are pulled or carried to the new site. Often they disagree with the idea and return, even pulling some colleague with them in their turn, only to find themselves forcibly removed yet again. This and other facts about ants' language, learning, and social organization will be discussed more fully in later chapters. There are more differences between the ant of popular belief and the ant of reality which must be cleared away first.

One such belief has already been indirectly mentioned. This is the fact that nearly every ant colony has more than one queen. It is still taught in schools and universities that ants, like bees, have a *Queen*. This is not true, however. Occasionally it is so, but it is the exception and not the rule, and such colonies are usually either uneconomic ones that are dying out, or newly-founded ones that are struggling for survival. Only a few species of ants habitually have a single queen. Even when, as happens in some cases, the colony is founded by a single queen ant, then as soon as it is succeeding and expanding towards a mature level of population, additional queens are adopted after the next marriage flights, or else virgin queens are mated with males inside the nest itself and given regal status.

In a large hillock of the British Wood Ant (*Formica rufa*, *L.*) there may be as many as a hundred queens. In a normal colony of the little Black Lawn Ant (*Acanthomyops niger*, *L.*) there are usually four or five mature egg-laying queens. The possession of several queens gives the ant colony a greater chance of survival than if a single queen had to be relied upon as with bees. But living as they do a terrestrial life and not an aerial one, they are much more liable to be the victims of such disasters as floods, fire, or having their nests trampled upon or disturbed by human and other animals. Also there is the constant toll of ant warfare. It is strange and rather sad that just as man is his own chief enemy, so is the ant its own greatest enemy. The ants are masters of the world of the immediate surface of the earth and the first few inches below it. They are the most widespread and successful insects in the world, and the most highly developed both mentally and socially; as a result, there often isn't enough room, and wars of expansion or for bare survival must be fought.

The success of the world of ants needs some explaining, both as to how it is achieved and what it means. It is best, perhaps, to begin by looking a little further into the realm of the Ant Kingdom. The scientists call this kingdom the *Formicidae*. That is the group name for all the ants. Being cousins of the Bees (*Apidae*), Wasps (*Vespidae*), and Ichneumon flies (*Ichneumonidae*), they are grouped with them, together with one or two lesser kingdoms, to form an Order of Insects, the *Hymenoptera*, which means literally the 'membrane-winged' insects.

The first thing to realize about the *Formicidae* is the number of species of ants which go to make up this kingdom. Up to the present (1952) about 15,000 species have been described and named, and some three hundred new species are described each year.

The ants are not just a vast group in the number of their individuals; they also differ considerably in their form and their habits. Indeed, the second point to realize is the diversity of their habits. There are Harvesting Ants and Slave-making Ants; there are Army Ants and ants which grow and eat mushrooms; there are ants which are parasites on other ants, and ants which live entirely by thieving from other ants; there are ants which live entirely by attacking Termite (so-called white ant) colonies and eating the inmates, and there are others who defend Termite colonies against these other ants while living as guests in the Termite mounds; there are ants 1/25th of an inch long and ants 1½ inches long; there are ants which are as heavily armoured and move as ponderously as a tortoise, and others that are so lightly armoured and move so fast that, when travelling at full speed, they leave the ground. The catalogue is almost unending, but one more item must be added separately, as it deserves: there are social ants and there are non-social ants, or at least barely social ones. The belief that all ants live in highly-developed societies is, of course, another popular myth. Actually there is a much greater range in types of ant societies and their degree of social development than is found, on a different level, in man.

The societies of the primitive ants contain only a few individuals, often only a dozen, or a few more or less. These primitive ants all belong to two 'sub-families', as the main family groups within the ants are termed. These two sub-families are the *Ponerinae* and the *Cerapachyinae*. Altogether there are eight sub-families which make up the ant family or kingdom, the *Formicidae*. They are: the *Ponerinae*, the most primitive of all ants; the *Cerapachyinae*, which link the *Ponerinae* to the Army Ants; the *Dorylinae*, the Army Ants of India, Africa, and South America; the *Myrmicinae*, largest and most diverse of all ant sub-families; the *Leptanillinae*, a small sub-family of microscopic army ants; the *Pseudomyrminae*, rare slender beauties which live between the bark and the trunks of trees; the *Dolichoderinae*, lightly-armed, fast-moving, darting, scavenger ants, found the world over; and finally the *Formicinae*, the cream of the ant kingdom, though some *Myrmicinae* might dispute this.

The Ponerine ants (*Ponerinae*) are all dwellers in the earth. They make no mounds over their nests, which are burrowed straight into the soil and usually have only two or three holes. Another feature which is common to all Ponerine ants is the absence of any special soldier forms like those found in the Myrmicine harvesting ants. Indeed, all the seventy odd genera of Ponerine ants have workers, males, and queens, which look very alike – that is, where there are three distinguishable castes. For example, in the genus *Diacamma*, one of the large Indian and Australian Ponerines, no queens exist. The egg-laying is undertaken by one or more workers. All worker ants are in fact degenerate females, and may be capable of laying eggs, but in none of the other sub-families are they capable of being fertilized by a male. As a result when the worker ants of other sub-families do lay eggs, these eggs are unfertilized ones and (because of the peculiar mechanism of sex-determination in the ants) turn into males. Very rarely do workers produce eggs parthenogenetically which develop into workers and they never lay eggs producing queens. That is except in the case of these primitive *Ponerinae* like *Diacamma*. The colonies of *Diacamma* consist of two or three hundred individuals who venture out each day on solitary hunting expeditions. Dull black, heavily-armoured creatures, two-thirds of an inch long, they feed on any kind of insect flesh. They largely neglect their grubs, feeding them by merely placing bits of insect flesh beside them. The societies of the Australian *Amblyopone* are even more primitive. Like the *Diacamma*, they have no special queens, and even the males work. At least they do just as much work for the primitive community as the worker-cum-queens. They go out and feed themselves and, like the workers, bring back some of the prey they have caught to the nest. While they are eating this the elongate active grubs grab bits and feed themselves.

There is very little of the social life here among these

primitive ants. Even that most characteristic feature of the life of social ants, regurgitation, is missing, for these solitary *Amblyopones* and *Diacammas*, and indeed most of the Ponerines, do not feed one another. Yet the most characteristic gesture in all antdom, especially the societies of the *Myrmicinae*, *Formicinae*, and *Dolichoderinae*, is the mutual feeding of one ant by another. It provides an important emotional bond. After a preliminary gesturing with the feelers in which the hungry ant seems to express her hunger, and the food-carrying ant her lowering resistance to parting with the contents of her crop, both ants raise themselves up high on their legs with heads extended upwards and forwards towards one another. Soon a drop of shining liquid honeydew appears from the mouth of the returning forager (for such the feeding ant usually is) and then rests a second between the extended mandibles of the two ants, while their tautly-stretched antennae (feelers) quiver in apparent ecstasy, then down it is sucked into the stomach of the grateful recipient. The food thus passed on is undigested, being kept in the communal stomach of the ant, the crop. This is separated from its own personal stomach, where digestion and feeding take place, by means of a valved apparatus (the gizzard), which is only capable of letting through a single drop of food at a time.

The frequency of this mutual feeding can be judged by feeding some yellow ants (say the British Yellow Lawn ants, *Acanthomyops umbratus*) on honey which is stained red or blue. Even if the number allowed to feed on the honey is limited to half a dozen individuals, within twenty-four hours the whole colony will be found to have bottoms coloured by the honey showing through their thin transparent armour.

The Ponerines share none of this mutual intercourse, nor its emotional ecstasy. Their communities are aggregations of individual hunters, held together rather by the accident (to them) of their hatching out together from their cocoons, than by any real social bond. They are in fact barely social insects. Their young grow up with them and remain with them when adult, and help excavate a new hollow or passage in the primitive nest, but there is little else that is social about their existence.

Most of these cave ants, as the Ponerines might be called, are large and heavily armoured with tough, thick skins, difficult for other insects to pierce. Because of their heavy armour, very like that of knights in the days of jousting, they often move slowly. The largest of all ants is *Dinoponera grandis* of the Amazons, nearly 2 inches long. When it walks it seems to move almost as if each step was a mechanical operation, involving a whirring of machinery and an ordering of all the different inclinations and stretchings of its joints so deliberate is its pace.

The Bulldog ants of Australia (*Myrmecia*) are also Ponerines. Large ants over an inch long and with protruding saw-like jaws, they live in colonies of larger size than most Ponerines. Their nests may contain between 500 and 2,000 individuals. Great disturbers of picnics, they are often brighter in colour than other Ponerines, being metallic blue or bright red and black combined, and have a sting a quarter of an inch long. Some species can jump considerable distances. Froggatt (1905) describes how *Myrmecia nigrocincta* will at the first alarm 'come jumping out of the side door' of their nest 'one after the other; like a pack of dogs, and fasten on to the first thing they come across.' This species, the best of the jumpers, will often jump distances of 7 or 8 inches while running along. Most of the *Myrmecia* can also swim for short distances and readily take to the water, a fact which may be connected with their living mainly in the coastal regions of Australia, where streams abound. With few exceptions they are rarely found very far inland.

Although these bulldog ants are better developed socially than most of the *Ponerinae*, and have proper queens, they do not feed one another; each individual must forage for itself. Even the queens do not receive the special attention that is their due amongst the truly social species of ants. They are not specially guarded, and leave the nest to forage for themselves. Being of altogether lower fertility than the petted queens of the other ant sub-families, they do not continuously lay eggs, but only produce them at somewhat infrequent intervals. Thus few eggs are lost during the queen's unhindered foraging. The history of the ants, their pre-history and the story of the evolution of their societies is the subject of the next chapter. There are other important facts which must be discussed before that story can be told.

The *Myrmecia*, like the majority of ant species, have a marriage flight, in which the queens fly high into the air and are chased by the males and fertilized. This marriage flight is an important event in the life of an ant colony, especially in the case of the large communities of the higher ants. It is these marriage flights which annually fill the newspapers with accounts of swarms of 'flying ants' invading homes and gardens. These flying ants are not a special species or group of species of ants. They are the males and queens of the ordinary ants of the garden and countryside enjoying their one day of nuptial bliss. There is a great variation in habit amongst the 15,000 different kinds of ants in the way the nuptial flights are carried out. Some ant species have either wingless males or wingless queens, and then either the males are carried on the backs of the queens, or the queens fly away after fertilization on the ground. Sometimes the males fly away to seek other colonies of the same species and fertilize their virgin queens. Yet basically the pattern is very similar in most species. The marriage flight takes place on a warm day in spring, summer, or autumn. It is usually towards the evening and when the weather is sultry with a premonition of thunder that the flight actually occurs, but the signs of preparation can be seen several hours, and sometimes several days, beforehand. The first sign is increasing excitement shown by the workers, large numbers of whom tend to rush hither and thither all round the area immediately surrounding the nest openings. When you are used to the habits of ants you will be able to observe this difference in their behaviour several days in advance, but not even the most inexperienced observer would fail to notice the change in their behaviour and their mounting excitement on the day itself. It gives the impression that the workers are patrolling every inch of the ground round the nest before allowing their royal charges to appear, with swarms of workers dashing out and quickly searching round and running back into the nest. In reality, of course, their behaviour is not so purposeful; they are excited and dash out of the nest, but the attraction of the virgin queens and males inside the nest soon draws them back.

Before the queens can escape the nest entrances must be enlarged to allow for the passage of their larger bodies. Their bodies may, in the *Formicinae* (the highest ants), be several times the size of the workers'. In the case of *Carebara*, one of the *Myrmicinae*, the queen is 7,000 times larger in volume than her minute worker offspring, but this is an extreme case and very exceptional. Normally the queens are from half as long again as the workers to twice as long, and very much fatter in proportion in both thorax and abdomen. But before their marriage flight the queens have wings, and these must not be damaged and necessitate a larger expansion of the doorways than would otherwise be necessary.

The males are usually smaller than the queens and may be either bigger, smaller, or the same size as the workers. In the primitive Ponerines, there is, as has been seen, little difference between the three castes (when all three castes occur) either in form or in size, and this is also the case in some of the *Myrmicinae*, and in nearly all the *Cerapachyinae* (the Ponerines' cousins) and the *Pseudomyrminae* (the beautiful graceful cousins of the *Myrmicinae*). The Doryline Army Ants are exceptional in having enormous wasp-like males three-quarters of an inch to an inch long, which are much larger than their workers and soldiers and most unlike, though not so different in size from, their peculiar monstrous wingless queens. Little is known of their mating habits. To return to the marriage flight: the enlargement of the doorways may start several days before the day of the wedding, or it may be left until the day itself. Usually a little is done beforehand and the job is finally completed at the last moment. As the passages leading to the doorways must also be enlarged, small heaps of earth collect round the entrances, and these are usually apparent at least on the preceding day. When the way is clear the males and queens begin to appear. Both sexes have humped backs to their thoraxes where the wing muscles are placed and two pairs of silvery membranous transparent wings. The individual males and queens drag behind them one, two, three, or more workers, who try to hold them to the ground as they test their wings, and at the same time drag them this way and that, clear of the entrances. More and more of the males and queens appear, and, fluttering their wings and turning on their caretakers, do their best to climb to the highest vantage spots around the nest. The workers themselves are present in their thousands swarming all over the ground. It is a day when little work is done and even the light-hating troglodyte workers of the Yellow Lawn Ant (*Acanthomyops mixtus*), never normally seen abroad, swarm in the bright sunlight with their males and queens. Many of the workers themselves behave as if they wished to fly, rushing to the topmost peaks of the surrounding blades of grass, heather, or other vegetation. The same events are, strangely, occurring in every surrounding nest of the species concerned. By some sensitive assessment of minute changes of humidity and temperature, a unanimous choice is mechanically and almost inevitably made by all these individual communities. This is important because it means that the flights of the different nests intermingle to form a common wedding and thus ensure the mixing of the males and queens from many nests and a proper measure of inter-marriage and avoidance of the dangers of in-breeding.

In a very few minutes from the first appearance of the winged forms, the first virgin queen takes off. At first she flies unsurely and may even make a false start and fall, or quickly land; but soon she is off again, followed in rapid succession by one after another of her nest-mates, and by the males. On the ground the two sexes are kept as carefully apart as possible, although sometimes a male gains a nearby queen and mates, despite the struggles of the workers to keep them apart. If this happens, the queen still flies, although the male may be damaged by the ferocity of the workers in the fracas.

Once spiralling upwards the queens fly strongly and to a great height, round and round, up and up, until in the bright sunlight they congregate, circling in smoke-like swarms. Caught by the males they are fertilized in the air, flying less easily with the additional weight, and often falling some way towards the ground before throwing them off and rising again, only to be caught and to fall once more. Eventually, after several such matings, the queens tire and finally fall to the ground, a fate which has already befallen many of the males.

Then the ground is covered with scurrying queens, mated and fully-fledged at last, and seeking some nook or cranny in which to shelter. They are not allowed back into the nest they left, and seek at least temporary safety. Either before doing this, or when some temporary resting-place is found, the queen completes the rites of her marriage. Standing still a moment, she gives her wings a vigorous twisting shake and off they fall. Her flying days are over and she must set about founding a new colony. Her disused wing muscles disintegrate and turn to fat on which in some cases she must live until her first brood mature and can go and forage and bring her food to eat. In such a case she seeks permanent quarters under a stone or in a hole and seals herself in a shallow cell, bricking the walls with earth mixed with her saliva. It will be several weeks before the first eggs are laid and some fourteen weeks more before the first workers can appear. During the whole of this period she must live on the resources of her own body or else eat the eggs, which she frequently does, delaying the final appearance of the mature offspring.

Ants found their colonies in numerous ways. The queens may, as has been said, be needed to increase the strength of their own or local colonies: then their life is an easy one, with no struggle for success; but this is not true colony foundation, which is the task of the majority of newly-mated queens and the reason for the marriage flight. The flight not only ensures a mixing of heredity, it ensures a spreading of the species. This despite the fact that perhaps only one queen in several thousands may succeed.

In some species the new queen becomes a temporary parasite in the nest of another species, hanging about the nest to gain some elements of their odour and then boldly entering despite attacks and placing herself on the back of one of the queens of her unwilling hosts. Here she is sacrosant and repays her freedom from interference by cutting off the head of her protector and calmly taking her place. Soon the colony has workers of both species on its tracks and then, as the new race grows in numbers, their hosts die out, failing to replace their own aged queens, and a new colony of the temporary parasite is formed. The Jet Black Ant of North America and Britain (*Acanthomyops fuliginosus*) founds its nest in this manner by entering the nests of the Yellow Lawn Ant already mentioned. *Carebara* takes scores of her tiny workers with her on her marriage flight, who later help her found her new colony.

The queen of *Polyergus*, the Amazon slave-maker, makes a single-handed slave-raid to steal cocoons of the slave species which soon hatch out to help her in her task. The American guest ant queen (*Leptothorax emersoni*) seeks out a nest of the red ant *Myrmica*, where she is dragged in willingly for the sake of the sweet secretions she exudes and which the red ants love to lick. She has an easy task, begging a drop of food from each red ant seeking pleasure.

The Wood ants (*Formica rufa*) usually return to the nest or seek a daughter colony, part in this case of the mother nest and not hostile, whence she soon sets out to a nearby site with a small group of workers to set up her new home. But she may become a temporary parasite of another species, or found her nest alone.

This latter is the normal mode of colony foundation and all the rest are variations from this basic pattern.

One more final myth must be killed, if it be still believed, at the beginning of this account of ant life. Ants live long lives: they do not die each season, and queen ants live longest of all. Sir John Lubbock (later Lord Avebury) kept one of his queens of the Large Black Ant (*Formica fusca*) for nearly fifteen years, and another for thirteen years. Queens of many species live to be eight or ten years old even under natural conditions, although these records of Lubbock remain so far the longest recorded span of ant life. It is probably safe to regard the usual span of a queen ant's life as between five and ten years. The workers live for a shorter period, but usually, if accident be avoided, for at least two and more often three or four years. Again, Lubbock has kept workers of the Large Black Ant for seven or eight years in captivity, and Donisthorpe, the present author, and many others, have kept known individuals for periods of four or more years. In the more dangerous life of freedom the accident rate is high, though, oddly, the job-finding excitement centre ants seem to have a better chance of survival than most and can be seen (duly marked) returning for several seasons to their accustomed task. Obviously their survival is important to the economic success of the colony. It ensures that next year's brood at least obtains the chance to learn the taking over of their tasks and to absorb the accumulation of their knowledge of choice foraging spots, trees for the pasturing of aphids, and other ant lore.

Thus ants are not exceptionally industrious, though they work hard, are individually varied, and can learn in a primitive way and have a social organization that works by simple means, not necessitating ordering about or reasoning. They start their life with a marriage flight, for the queen produces the worker offspring as well as future queens. They have almost as many diverse habits as man, though they have no language and don't use tools. Lastly, they have a history of social evolution from cave-dwelling sub-social communities to the growth of the complex societies of the higher ants, the *Formicinae*, which is every bit as fascinating as that of Man. It is the first part of this story which will be told in the next chapter.

CHAPTER 2

Ant History

*

Two hundred million years ago, the pre-ant wandered the plains and swamps of Central Asia. Little is known about it, but it undoubtedly was a predator, eating other insects, and was a large heavy insect, something like the Scoliid wasps of to-day. It was in fact also the pre-Scoliid.

Gradually the climate became warmer and the flowers and insects began to flourish. These were the days of the great burgeoning of life and land emergence of the Jurassic age, some 150 million years ago. It was during this period that the great Alaskan land bridge joining Asia, and thereby Europe, to America appeared.

The pre-ant, male and female, flourished and bred in ever-increasing numbers as the sun shone and the swamps and the reptiles began to disappear and more land was pushed above the sea on every side. These were aeons of destiny, for one day, somewhere in this vast plain of Eurasia, a pre-ant oddity appeared. At first this peculiar brood seemed like weaklings, for, after their first few flights, their females' wings proved weak and snapped off at the joints. However, fate made up for the loss, perhaps by granting them extra fertility, perhaps by means of the extra food available on the many areas of newly-drying ground. These odd pre-ants survived. Although born in each generation with wings, the females were forced to live a terrestrial life because of their inherent weakness. Indeed, most of them probably lost their wings soon after their adult birth. The males, however, could roam at will and were handicapped by their wings on the ground. Shorter-lived, they pursued their merry aerial course awhile, strayed far, and soon died.

Not long afterwards – at least by the end of the Jurassic period or the beginning of the Cretaceous, thirty million years later – another odd brood was born. These creatures had a real deformity – a hard armoured knot in the middle of their waists. This time both males and females were affected: these were the first true ants. The knot proved a great advantage to the females in their hunting expeditions. Indeed they flourished better than their immediate ancestors on its account, for it protected their previously thin and exposed waists from attack and severance. The wings still appeared each generation, but were soon lost and the knot stayed as the hall-mark of antdom.

With their change in form and their reliance on terrestrial hunting there came another change – whether before or after full antdom was achieved is not known: the adult brood took to staying together, and not wandering off singly or in pairs. They scraped out a small communal hollow, and though they went out singly to forage, they returned to this primitive home each night.

The long voracious worm-like grubs, offspring of a mixed group of pairings, also developed a peculiar, seemingly rather unimportant gland near their mouths, and their skins became moist. The adult ants seemed quite to like the taste of the minute drops of liquid expressed from this gland and the liquid wetting their skins, and would occasionally feed the grubs, apparently just for the sake of tasting the drop exuded, and lick them because of the taste of their wetness. Later, as will be seen, this trivial event proved to be one of the most important milestones in ant history.

The warmth of the climate – rather more than that of the present day, but not greatly in excess of it – continued, and other changes occurred with ever-increasing speed. The success of the small ant communities had been immediate. They began to dominate the immediate face of the earth around them. The communities never became too large, because when the numbers exceeded a dozen or two, some took to staying away in new hollows nearby, and others copied them. Also some got scattered when they flew after their birth and were unable to return because their wings broke off and they had flown too far away. At first this meant that some males and females never found a mate, because they flew singly and were lost. However, the tendency to fly as soon as they hatched, mature, from their cocoons and their wings had hardened, and the immediate wakening of their sexual appetites meant that the first flight usually became a mating chase: a habit that soon, how it is not known, became bred genetically as firmly as the knot, as one of the ant characteristics. Ant history is full of such genetic fixations of what were at first undoubtedly chance deeds in no way genetically determined. This is a subject which so far has been little investigated by scientists. How important and vast a field it will one day prove, will be seen as the story of this single group of animals, the ants, unfolds.

Thus, anyway, was the marriage flight born. The Ponerine ants as we know them to-day were in existence: more primitive in form and habit than most of the Ponerine genera, it is true, but not very different from the Indian *Diacamma*, the Australian *Amblyopone*, and the kindred *Stigmatomma* of the American tropics.

The ants were indeed succeeding, and as they succeeded so their unsettled germ plasm continued to throw out sports. At the same time the ever-increasing numbers of small communities and their habit of mating in the air, and often falling to the ground far from home, led to a vast spreading of their kindred over the face of the globe.

Amblyopone at least is a relic of these earliest days. Once itself a successful and abundant ant, it spread out to the perimeter of antdom. It has survived only in Australia, cut off from the other land masses seventy to a hundred million years ago, and thus more poorly populated with other ants, and also equable enough throughout all the succeeding ages to support an insect that could not survive temperatures either much colder or much hotter than those under which it originally flourished. It is almost blind, with stubby legs and antennae and the simplest of knots on its waist, almost fused into its abdomen, with its bulging first segment almost forming a second knot. The body itself is thickly armoured with few sutures and none of the complicated scalloping and angling met in many of the ants.

The trail of these early migrations is more clearly pictured by the spread of the still queenless *Diacamma* whose later species survive in India, Burma, and Madagascar as well as in New Guinea and Australia. Madagascar, like Australia, has long been separated from the larger land groups. Already separated from Africa early in Triassic days of the pre-ant, it is the largest remaining piece of the old continent of Lemuria, once joined to India across what is now the Indian Ocean. Although *Diacamma* survives to-day, its present species are for the most part later developments. This ability to develop species very similar to the mother form, but more varied and able to survive a greater range of the warmer temperatures, accounts for its success in sur-viving to-day, more certainly and more widespread than *Amblyopone*. Yet *Diacamma* is, despite this, also degenerate, unlike the Australian Bulldog ants (*Myrmecia*), who have re-mained a virile, generalized, and more socially developed relic of the oldest form of ant civilization.

The locality in which each particular genus first deve-loped is not known. But from the records of their distribution it is clear that most, if not all, of the ant genera which we know to-day existed before the end of the Cretaceous period, or at least by the beginning of the Eocene, seventy million years ago. One reason for this belief is the occurrence of representatives of the *Dolichoderinae* and *Formicinae*, most recently evolved and socially the most highly developed of the ant sub-families in Australia. Yet there was no land route to Australia after the Eocene, and invasion by other means could only have been very slight. The separation of the Americas occurred much later and the Alaskan land bridge, of which the Aleutian islands are a surviving relic, existed throughout the Miocene and Pliocene eras, thirty-five and fifteen millions years ago respectively.

Some species must have been fully developed by this time, for the three ubiquitous ants, the Ponerine *Odontomachus haematodes*, the Formicine *Camponotus* (*Myrmoturba*) *maculatus*, and the Myrmicine *Solenopsis geminata* are found on each of the major land masses with only the slightest local varia-tion of form.

Before this great flowering of the genera could occur, other events took place. Back once more in the Cretaceous period 120 million years ago, the major changes that set the main lines of development were taking place. The males remained at first unaffected, but the females began to alter. One or two of them in each brood proved, not unnaturally, more fertile than the rest and because of this fertility produced a greater number of eggs. This was a hindrance to their foraging and so they tended to go out less and to stay at home more. Or it may be that the tendency to stay at home became inherent, even at this early stage, genetically established by natural selection, because to go out foraging would endanger the eggs and cause them to get lost and wasted. Whichever way it happened the important thing is its occurrence. They needed food and took it from their returning, less fertile, female colleagues and from the males. Once established, the characteristic grew quite naturally, for their eggs also produced more fertile offspring. But, and it is a big but, another event must have occurred simultaneously, the lessening of the fertility of the mass of females; for in each generation (and soon only once or twice a year) only comparatively few of these specially fertile females were born. They are the ant queens. Their less fertile colleagues are the workers, who still, if need be, can lay an egg or two, though almost never a fertile one. Because the sexes are determined by whether the egg is or is not fertilized (male unfertilized : female and worker fertilized) these eggs produce only male offspring. With the limitation of fertility to queens, the males have become of little use to the community except at mating time. If the males had been wingless and, perhaps, less interested in their maleness, they might still have survived as useful working members of the community. But the males remained unchanged. They kept their wings and flew on the marriage flight with the queens, but failed to satisfy her greater need of sperm. Each queen now needed five or six inseminations and so even their claim to consortship, living beside their mates, was lost. Whether because of the danger of having numerous males with their more active sexual rôle near a few females, or because of their probably already shorter life becoming shortened yet further, the males now became solely agents of fertilization. The male was accepted until his task was fulfilled, then forbidden shelter and even attacked if he tried to return. Yet, oddly enough, in the few species where wingless males are found, they may survive for their whole few months' span of life, happily accepted in the nest. Such is the case in the West Indian Myrmicine *Cardiocondyla*, several Ponerines of the genus *Ponera*, and the European Myrmicine parasitic ant, *Anergates*, and the guest ant of the Wood Ants, *Formicoxenus*. In the latter case they almost seem to play a worker-like rôle after their mating. But the male never learnt to feed a colleague and so must always have remained an outcast.

As the worker caste developed in numbers and importance, and the queen's fertility increased to yield a truly massive egg-production (often equivalent to a thousand eggs each day), so the rôle of the brood began to play a more and more important part in the community. The glandular fluid that exuded from the mouths of the grubs when they were fed was more than ever sought by the scurrying workers and was provided in ever-increasing quantities. Each worker who fed a larva obtained a treat in exchange. The grubs became important and beyond price for the sake of this delicious treat. They must be the first thing saved, even at the risk of life, if the colony is attacked, and if they pout with hunger, then they must be fed as quickly as possible until the pouting stops. Needless to say, licking and feeding them became a great rite. The protection gained by the grubs during their worm-like stage even survived through their pupal stage – in fact until they became recognizable as fellow ants.

All this, of course, reflected in turn on the queens as the producers of these delightful treasures. The ant queens are not loved for themselves, but for what they produce. The colony becomes lethargic and dispirited in their absence because of the lack of numerous offspring, not because of the absence of an extra large royal personage. Hence the

The Ant World

killing of old and no longer productive queens. For the same reason a wounded queen may also be killed.

A worker that really takes the place of the queen in quantity of production, as sometimes happens (especially in the case of some *Myrmicinae* and *Formicinae*), is treated just as royally despite the fact that she is unable to produce queens for the marriage flight. It is not at all clear if such workers which take over on the death of the queen in a colony reduced to having only a single queen are fertilized or not. Certainly workers can, on rare occasions, lay eggs which are diploid, having two sets of chromosomes as against the single set found in the males, by parthenogenesis, which means in the absence of male sperm – without having been fertilized. But in such cases relatively small numbers are produced, at least according to all records of the occurrence in captive colonies. The event is exceptional, most eggs produced by workers turning, as might be expected, into males. Worker egg-laying is a frequent occurrence, but the numbers of eggs laid are nearly always small.

This mutual exchange of food between grub and worker, of sustenance in the one case and pleasure in the other, may even provide the explanation for another fundamental factor in ant life, the mutual regurgitation of undigested food from one ant to another. It is impossible to guess when and how the crop developed. The crop is the social stomach at the bottom of the alimentary canal which is separated from the true feeding stomach, where digestion occurs, by a valve, which is termed the gizzard. It is present in all ants, even the most primitive, and in the males, although, as already mentioned, they have never learnt to utilize it for regurgitation. Obviously the presence of the crop made the division of labour in the ant colony possible. It gave the foragers a basket in which to carry their unadulterated wares home to their nest mates, and meant that a few workers could undertake a task that would otherwise occupy almost the entire colony if a large brood and many queens were present.

But this mutual regurgitation is more than the feeding of a hungry ant by a returning forager. It is, as any student of ants will tell you, the symbolic action of the ant colony. It goes on constantly wherever ants meet, even if both have well filled crops, and in the case of a stranger ant, placed within the gates by some experimenter, it is the symbol of final acceptance and unity with the colony.

May not the mutual feeding between the adult and the grub have played some part in both the foundation of this habit and its significance? Certainly it has a significance in ant pyschology for which even scientists have failed to find any other word than 'emotional'. Its importance is the same in such ants as the leaf cutting ants (*Attini*) of South America, who grow their food at home within the nest itself, and do not use their crops for foraging, carrying home aloft only a single piece of leaf each which they use to form the basic mulch for their mushroom spores.

Except in the most primitive genera of the *Ponerinae*, all these basic habits are found more or less developed in every kind of ant. In the Ponerines the queen, if she exists as a separate caste, is little different from the workers, and is not so fertile, and because of this, and the low stage of development of the mutual feeding of the grubs, is treated indifferently. There is also relatively little regurgitation between worker and worker.

Except, however, for these poor early relics all ants share these fundamental qualities of ant behaviour. Even the later *Ponerinae* have them, for it must not be forgotten that they have continued to evolve along their ancient line, though never to the same extent. These traits must therefore have been established in the early days of the late Cretaceous period, a hundred million years ago.

They opened the way to unbounded success and with that success came great diversity both of form and habit. The *Ponerinae*, it is true, changed little, and their closest cousins of the *Cerapachyinae* remain much like them and have bravely lingered on. But even they provided a link to another powerful and virile sub-family, the *Dorylinae*, whose marching legions are the scourge of Tropical Africa and America. The *Myrmicinae*, in numbers of genera and species the greatest

TIME	TREE
Triassic *190 million*	**PRE-ANT**

	TIME	TREE
MESOZOIC	**Jurassic** *150 million* *Warm*	*Nuptial flight originates* — *Females' wings weakened* — *Waist-knot appears* — *Origin of mutual grub-adult feeding*
	Cretaceous *120 million*	Amblyopone **PRIMITIVE PONERINAE** — *Queen's fertility develops and worker's fertility degenerates* — *Primitive Ponerinae completely isolated* — Protaneuretus — Dolichoderinae — *Primitive Myrmicinae* — *Great development of mutual feeding*
TERTIARY	**Eocene** *70 million Warmer than present*	
	Oligocene *50 million Very much warmer than today*	PONERINAE · CERAPACHYINAE · DORYLINAE · LEPTANILLINAE · DOLICHODERINAE · FORMICINAE · MYRMICINAE · PSEUDOMYRMINAE
	Miocene *35 million Cooler again but warmer than Eocene*	
CENOZOIC	**Pliocene** *15 million Warmer again, then rapidly cooler*	
	Pleistocene *(Glacial)* *1 million*	
	Holocene *(Recent)*	

			SPREAD		
Australian Australia	*Oriental* India, Burma, Malaya, etc.	*Ethiopian* Africa, inc. and south of Abyssinia	*Palaearctic* Eurasia	*Nearctic* Temperate N. America	*Neotropical* Tropical Americas, N. and S.
LAND BRIDGE			Pre-ant LAND BRIDGE		
LAND BRIDGE			ANT (Primarily Ponerinae) LAND BRIDGE		
LAND BRIDGE			Bembridge Beds LAND BRIDGE		
NO BRIDGE			Baltic		
S. geminata.	C. Myrmoturba maculatus.		Amber NO BRIDGE O. haemotodes. Wyoming Colorado Amber		
NO BRIDGE	Polymorphism developed in *Dorylinae*		Tropical forms disappearing slowly Sicilian Amber NO BRIDGE *Leptomyrmex,* still present in Sicily LAND BRIDGE	Florrisant Amber	
Polymorphism of worker developed in *Formicinae* and *Myrmicinae*					
NO BRIDGE			LAND BRIDGE		
NO BRIDGE			NO BRIDGE		
NO BRIDGE			NO BRIDGE		
NO BRIDGE			NO BRIDGE		

Left margin vertical labels: Land emerging — Land sinking — Marine Age of the sub-families, were also split off to follow their own development during these early days. The *Dolichoderinae*, first of the stingless ants (with one sting-bearing genus, *Aneuretus*) followed next, and from their roots flowed the dominating *Formicinae*, youngest and most successful of all the ants, with their greater adaptability to both cold and heat, and their greater mental abilities and vast polycalic colonies of scores, or even hundreds, of nests linked together as a great nation.

In the time between the development of these fundamentals of antdom just described and the end of the Eocene age nearly seventy million years ago, a developmental period of between thirty and fifty million years, there developed nearly 400 ant genera, subdivided in some cases into sub-genera of almost equal standing. Some 600 major units, for there were close on 250 sub-genera, were fixed in this great period of expansion and success. A few sub-genera – say 50 odd – may have arisen since, although not much later, and except for the actual species that we know to-day, the main characters, both anatomical and behavioural, of all the ants were fixed in the latter part of the Cretaceous and before the beginning of the Eocene age.

Something of this diversity and of how the lines can be traced must now be told. Of necessity some part of the story of the appearance of the various species, both fossil and surviving, will be told in passing, if only by way of illustration. Reference to the simple chart should help the reader to keep a clear picture of the timing and inter-relationships of the many events.

The late Jurassic and early Cretaceous period, during which this part of the history of the ants reached its completion, was one of land emergence and the existence of vast continental areas and land bridges. Every region of land that we know to-day was accessible by means of these bridges. Africa was, as it remains to-day, joined to the Eurasian home of the ants by means of the Arabian land bridge; the Alaskan land bridge was broad and well established and the Americas formed a more solid block than they do to-day. Whether or not there was any bridge between S. America and New Zealand remains a matter of dispute, but if it did exist, it played a relatively unimportant part in the distribution of the ants.

Towards the end of the Cretaceous period, this position was reversed and the land was re-invaded by the sea. Between the middle of the Cretaceous and a time shortly after the beginning of the Eocene period, Australia was separated from the rest of the continental masses, never to be rejoined. The land bridge between Eurasia and North America disappeared and Eurasia itself was split into at least two separate parts, being divided northwards along the line of the Caspian Sea. Only southern India remained above water and probably only southern Africa, with one or more large isolated hunks of its present western part. Greenland was above water, also a triangular mass around the British Isles close beside and perhaps joined to Scandinavia, and a largish strip of what is now Northern Russia. The Americas were divided into at least two major parts, northern and southern, and South America may have been further divided by a wide sea along the line of the Amazon. The largest land mass was that of Asia, separated from southern India, but otherwise comprising much of its present territory.

Because of the widespread sea, warm currents flowed throughout the earth bringing warm temperatures to the poles. In general the temperature was rather warmer than at present, but more equally distributed. Towards the end of this period and during the Oligocene, fifty million years ago, the climate became very warm, much warmer than to-day. Fifteen million years later in the Miocene age it became cooler, though still warmer than at the beginning of this Marine period, in which vast seas covered much of the earth. By this time the land was once more emerging from the sea and with it began the establishment of the general temperature ranges that we know to-day. When the ice ages came in the Pleistocene age, a million years ago, a great coldness spread over much of the earth, but the tropics still remained hot, if cooler than at present, and the graded temperature distribution was in general unaffected. At the time of this deluge, all the sub-families and most of the genera of the ants were already scattered throughout the globe, but some were only just beginning their development and others were already approaching their maximum degree of diversity and success.

The amber of North America, the Baltic, and of Sicily, and the copal of South Africa and Zanzibar, contain many ants and help to elucidate some of the story. This amber and copal is solidified resin which enclosed many ants as it dropped from the conifers of Europe and North America, and the Zanzibar *Trachylobium*. The oldest amber is the so-called Baltic amber of Europe. Although commonest in the regions surrounding the Baltic Sea, it is also found in more southern regions. It is of late Eocene and Miocene age, fifty to sixty million years old. The amber from Colorado and Wyoming in North America is a little younger, from forty to fifty million years old, and that from Sicily and the North American Florissant beds belongs to the Miocene age, thirty-five million years ago. The Zanzibar copal is at most five or six million years old.

In the Baltic amber, tropical ants mingle with ants which to-day dominate the cooler Palearctic and Nearctic regions of Eurasia and North America. They are fewer in number, but present in some considerable quantity. In the later Sicilian amber, on the other hand, the tables are reversed, the tropical ants are dominant. But the major lesson to be learnt from the study of these fossil ants is that the ants of those days were much like the ants of to-day: of the fifty genera represented less than twenty are extinct. Even the species are similar.

The *Ponerinae* are poorly represented, but provide one interesting relic, *Prionomyrmex longiceps*. This ant from the Baltic amber is one of the simplest types of Ponerines known. Large, very hairy, and with well developed but simple mandibles and a deep constriction at the end of the first segment of its abdomen, it might almost be the primitive ancestor of the Australian Bulldog ants. On the whole, there are few Ponerine relics from what must in fact have been the tail end of their most successful period, but this is no doubt because they lived and hunted then, as they still do, in the earth – not climbing trees, nor building large nests. Also their colonies were small and in most species they had no proper marriage flight. The species most often trapped are those which climbed trees, or landed on them while flying. Another important find in the amber was that of a primitive Dolichoderine ant *Protaneuretus*, a cousin of the present-day relic *Aneuretus simoni*, solitary representative of its genus which is the only ant of the *Dolichoderinæ* to possess a sting. Very similar to the more primitive types of Ponerine ants, it confirms the belief that the *Dolichoderinae* evolved directly from the ancient Ponerine stock.

The existence of another *Dolichoderinae* in the Sicilian amber, the Australian *Leptomyrmex*, which to-day is confined to the Australian deserts, shows that this genus, now surviving only in areas early isolated from the main land mass, was then still clinging to a bare existence in face of the ever-increasing competition of more modern forms. Another such survival, the Formicine *Gesomyrmex*, was even first described from the Baltic amber and then, some twenty years later, was found to have a living representative in Borneo! The Myrmicine ants found in the amber are as complex in strucure – the wealth of their spines, odd formations of their heads (adapted for blocking doorways), and the sculpturing of their bodies – as any found to-day. Even ants milking greenflies have been found. Only one modern factor of importance is missing: there are no soldier ants, no large and small workers or other diverse forms in the ants of the amber. The Myrmicine harvesting ants *Pheidole* and *Pheidologeton*, and the Formicine *Camponotus*, which to-day have a large range of worker forms, are present in numbers, but without this variation.

The Doryline Army ants, on the other hand, have not been found among the definitely identifiable amber fossils, and it seems probable that their well developed sickle-jawed soldiers were already scavenging the earth in more southerly regions.

The fauna of both Europe and of North America in those days of the early Miocene age was predominantly that which we know as tropical and Australian to-day. It was the fauna of the hot East and the Malay Archipelago, intermingled with the Australian forms, that failed to survive even there. In the northernmost region, the last flowerings of the evolution of the ant genera were struggling for space, but by the end of the Miocene age, thirty million years later, they had obtained the domination of the northern regions of Asia, Europe, North America and the Siberian plateau. Even the few already isolated in Australia managed to survive, although without the same effective success which even their immediate ancestors achieved. Such genera were the Formicine *Camponotus* and *Formica*, and their immediate ancestors, the Dolichoderine *Iridomyrmex*. An outline of the history of all the many forms of ants must needs be in part speculative, but much certainty can be gained from a knowledge of the present fauna, coupled with such facts as those above.

Primitively, the Ponerine ant of the early Cretaceous period had, as has been seen, two simple forms, the male and female. Later the worker developed as the female fertility became segregated into a few individuals called queens. At this time all the ants on the earth were still *Ponerinae*. The workers had wasp-like heads with two elbowed feelers mounted towards the sides of the frontal part, a set of poorly-developed compound eyes (made up of several facets or lenses) on each side of the head, and one, two, or three solitary eyes on the top of the back end of their heads. The thorax was joined to the head by a neck inserted into a hollow underneath the hind end. It was very simple in structure, narrowing hindwards, elongate, and almost cylindrical. The front end was rounded to form the shoulders, as was the hind end, into which was inserted the narrow tube of the waist. This waist, or petiole, to give it its scientific term, soon expanded to form the large protective knot, or node. This did not decrease to its original thinness to form the secondary waist to the abdomen, as in the later ants. In all ants the visible abdomen is termed the gaster because all the waist and even the last rounded section of the thorax are historically (much farther back than the pre-ant) part of the abdomen. The abdomen was made of a series of overlapping sections, concertinaed into one another. The first of these sections was (and always is) the largest, and in the Ponerines forms almost a second knot, but is joined directly to the rest of the beetroot-shaped abdomen, with no further waist. At the hind end of the gaster was the sting and at the front end of the head two sets of jaws, an inner one hidden by an armoured plate, the clypeus, to masticate its food, and a large outer set shaped like a somewhat straightened pair of scythes. The six legs were attached in pairs to the thorax, each pair being attached to one of its three divisions which were at that time barely marked by three slight sutures. Each leg had five parts, coxa, trochanter, femur, tibia, and tarsus; and each front pair of legs had a small comb-like structure at the base of each femur, with which the ant cleaned its feelers and other legs. The males and queens were little different except for their appropriate genitalia and the possession of two pairs of wings, a large forward pair and a smaller hind pair, necessitating a more bulging thorax to carry their muscles and some small disarranging of the armour with consequently more numerous sutures in order to allow for their insertion. That is the primitive ant and the basic external structure of all ants.

Undoubtedly the first breaking away from this general picture occurred in the development of an even more heavily-armoured sluggish form of ant. Such an ant is *Phyracaces*, and its cousin *Sphinctomyrmex* from India, blind and living entirely underground. The back of the thorax has become a single tough flattened plate, and the knot on the petiole is a heavy, slightly rounded quadrangle, fully as wide as both thorax and the equally heavily-armoured gaster. With stumpy legs and short, thickened feelers these ants look and move rather like some barely articulated World

War I tank. Their colonies are small and such hunting as they do is undertaken either in the dark or underground within close reach of their primitive single-chambered nest. Usually they have small weak jaws. If they are attacked they lie still, playing 'doggo' and depending on their armour for protection. *Cerapachys*, the genus which gives this sub-family its name, is somewhat more active and more success-ful. It has four sub-genera and a few dozen species. There were probably never more than a dozen *Cerapachyine* genera, of which seven survive to-day, spread out in odd local regions, all over the globe. The lack of any proper waist be-tween the knot and the gaster is a relic from the tribe *Am-blyoponini*, which contains *Amblyopone* and its kindred genera, basic stock of the *Ponerinae*. The name *Phyracaces*, incident-ally, is only a transposition of the letters in the word *Cerapachys* : in such ways do scientists sometimes seek inspir-ation for the names with which to puzzle the student.

Oddly, it was from this slow-moving stock that the swiftly-marching nomads of the ant world sprang. The *Dorylinae* retain the characteristics of an ill-separated knot (at any rate in the workers), heavy armour, and no covering for the point of insertion of the antennae into their heads, and, strangely, their blindness. Although they often cover dis-tances of more than a mile in a day on their foraging raids, the worker, soldier and queen Army Ants are nearly blind. Confined to the tropics of South-East Asia, Africa, and South America, they are prolific in numbers, if not in genera and species. Their males are large vespine creatures, often an inch and a third long, and their queens are wing-less monsters. So different in form are the males and queens of these ants that for a long time they were thought to belong to different genera from the workers, and the male was even classified as a wasp or a Velvet ant (*Mutillid*). The habits of these *Dorylinae* are described in a special section in a separ-ate chapter (p. 85). Obviously they were one of the earliest offshoots of the family tree, evolving from the *Cerapachyinae* soon after their own segregation from the earliest Ponerines. They are a very primitive form of ant, making crude nests scraped hurriedly from the ground, and have little of the normal social life found in ant communities. The relationship between brood and workers is, however, well developed, although that between the workers themselves is poorly so: a reflection, perhaps, of the fact that although the Doryline workers are given the attractive exudate by the grubs when they feed them, they do not feed them by regurgitating food from their crops, but by presenting chunks of insect flesh to them. The lack of the habit of regurgitation in the *Dorylinae* is an indication of their primitive state of development. Their nomadic habits continue throughout the year in cycles of about seven weeks each. Half the time is spent resting and half raiding, and the home is moved each day. They are unique in the ant world. Peculiar forms of queens and males are often found amongst the ants, as will be seen, but those of the *Dorylinae* are certainly extraordinary. Their soldiers are found freely in the Zanzibar copal of five to six million years ago, and it seems probable that the soldier form developed at an earlier stage of the Dorylines' evolution than in the case of the Myrmicine harvesters and the pastoral Formicine *Camponotus*. Despite their apparent success during an actual passage through a territory, they cannot compete with their more highly communalized brethren, and this and their inability to survive in a non-tropical climate had caused their relegation to those areas.

Some time in the days of the early evolution of the *Dorylinae* a microscopic race appeared. More close to their Cerapachyine ancestors than most of the surviving *Dorylinae*, the Lilliputian *Leptanillinae* are also army ants. Left stranded in Corsica by the retreat of the tropical Indo-Malayan fauna, they survived to continue their raids on even more microscopical insects. It was the discovery of their males and queens that put the designation of those of their cousins, the *Dorylinae*, to rights.

The appearance of the *Cerapachyinae* throughout all the faunas of the world indicates a central origin. Their evolution can be safely said to have occurred near the home of the ants in Eurasia. It is, however, strange that there is no trace of the *Dorylinae* in Australia, for they certainly evolved long before the isolation of Australia, but their limitation to the western part of the Far East and their lesser success there as compared with that in both Africa and the tropics of the Americas points to an early move away from their place of origin. The early Doryline was born like the early Cerapachyine progenitor in Eurasia and quickly moved both southwards into Africa and eastwards across the Aleutian land bridge into the Americas. Its non-appearance in the Sicilian or Baltic ambers, when other tropical ants are frequently found, suggests an early drive outwards from the homeland towards the south. There was little communication between the Ethiopian fauna of central and southern Africa and the northern Indo-Malayan fauna after the earliest days (few of the Dolichoderine ants so common in the latter being found in Africa), and the warmer parts of the Americas were frequently isolated by the succeeding geological changes. It may be that early in the days of the Indo-Malayan fauna the Dorylines were here also driven south and perished in the subsidence and flooding of Lemuria, leaving the present relic of Indian Dorylines behind. But from Eurasia they came and the majority marched early from it.

Coincident with the events just told, another branching occurred. The knot of the Ponerines was now more clearly defined than in the *Amblyoponini* and had a true waist behind it, but the first section of the gaster, though clearly marked from the later ones by a deep suture, remained the first section of the gaster. A group arose in which this was altered and the suture deepened until a second knot, clearly separated from the gaster by a following waist, was formed. Thus was born the post-petiole and the immense sub-family *Myrmicinae*. The post-petiole was, of course, only the outward sign of the event, although not without its importance in the realm of behaviour, for it increased the mobility of the hind end of the body with its important weapon of offence, the sting, while at the same time maintaining an

adequate degree of protection for the waist. The chief factors in the revolution which the *Myrmicinae* brought with
them into the ant world were physiological and social. The
relationship between the grubs and the workers reached a
level of importance previously unknown. Regurgitation of
food became for the first time the order of the day amongst
the workers, and, in the more highly-developed genera, in
the feeding of the brood. The greater attention paid to the
brood and their consequent greater security is reflected in
the fact that the pupae are, for the first time in ant history,
naked and not enclosed in cocoons. This is the case in the
most primitive *Myrmicinae*. On the other hand, the grubs of
the Myrmicine ants are still more or less elongate, though less
so than those of the Ponerines, Cerapachyines, and Dorylines.

The *Myrmicinae* are the most diverse of all the ant sub-
families. No fewer than 115 genera, divided into two sections, twenty tribes and ten sub-tribes, are known. Their
range of anatomical form is vast and that of their habits
considerable. They are found all over the globe and have
both purely tropical, sub-tropical, temperate, and near-
arctic species. Nevertheless, they are limited by the very
fact of their early evolution from the early Ponerines. Of the
twenty tribes only eight possess more than a few genera. Of
these eight tribes one, the *Leptothoracini*, consists almost entirely of guest ants and parasitic species; another, the *Dace-
tini*, consists of a small group of minute picturesquely and
heavily-armoured troglodyte ants, often parasitic, and living
in small colonies whose numbers rarely exceed 100 individuals. A third tribe, the *Myrmecinini*, comprises ten genera of primitive troglodytes which also live in small colonies
and are exceptionally heavily armoured and cowardly. A
fourth of these eight tribes, that of the *Tetramoriini*, is a
somewhat more successful collection of nine genera of
primitive hunters. Again, the colonies are usually smallish,
rarely containing more than a few hundred individuals,
except in the case of the cosmopolitan genus *Tetramorium*,
represented in Britain by the Square-Shouldered ant, *T.
caespitum*, inhabitant of the sandy heaths of the New Forest.

In the case of this genus the colonies are populous and may number ten or more thousand individuals, but although they sometimes cultivate the root aphids on the subterranean roots of plants within their nests, they remain primarily carnivorous. Two genera of the tribe, *Harpagoxenus* and *Strongylognathus*, are the only Myrmicine ants known to make slave raids. But both genera are degenerate, scarcely capable of active fighting, and in one species, *S. diveri*, are reduced to virtual parasitism. Their habits will be discussed more fully when the slave-making raids of the *Formicinae* are described.

To the remaining four tribes, the *Pheidolini*, the *Solenopsidini*, the *Pheidologetini*, and the *Attini*, must be added that of the *Crematogastrini*, which contains the single genus *Crematogaster*, and the roll of the truly successful *Myrmicinae* is complete. It is possible to reduce the limits of success even farther; only the ten genera *Aphaenogaster*, *Messor*, *Pheidole*, *Pheidologeton*, *Crematogaster*, *Monomorium*, *Solenopsis*, *Cyphomyrmex*, *Acromyrmex* and *Atta* are truly dominant highly social genera like the majority of the genera of the *Formicinae* and a few like *Iridomyrmex* and *Dolichoderus* of the *Dolichoderinae*. Of these ten genera the first four are harvesting ants and the last three are fungus-growing (or leaf-cutting) ants, and the latter are limited in their range to the tropics of America. Only in *Crematogaster*, *Pheidole* (not always a harvester), *Monomorium*, and *Solenopsis* is maximal social development, range, and success like that of the great Formicine genera *Camponotus*, *Polyrhachis*, *Prenolepis*, *Formica*, *Acantholepis*, *Oecophylla*, to which even the entirely Palearctic and Nearctic *Acanthomyops* approached. The only Myrmicine genus with more than 100 species is *Solenopsis*, yet the Formicine genus *Camponotus* has over thirty-five sub-genera and several hundreds of species.

Obviously the *Myrmicinae* underwent much early development before the *Formicinae* appeared. Their diversity is expressed more at the level of anatomy than at that of social behaviour. The specialized habits of harvesting and mushroom-growing would have remained curiosities, of much less interest and considerably lessened importance, if it had not been for the later accompaniment of the progressive evolution of the characteristics of social behaviour. The development of the specialized soldier caste and of workers of varying size and form during the last fifteen million years (some time after the Sicilian amber) is paralleled in the *Formicinae* and is an expression of this social evolution, having little or no effect on the fundamental structure of the division of labour and social organization of the colonies. Without the previous establishment of the basic structure of the social organization, worker polymorphism (the production of many forms) would have proved of no benefit to the communities and would not have survived.

The *Myrmicinae* show their evolution in the diversity of their genera; the *Formicinae*, on the contrary, show theirs in the diversity of their species and the large number of species found in each genus. In the *Myrmicinae* are found primitive tribes and genera, more well-developed tribes and highly-developed genera. In the *Formicinae* the picture is different. There are less than forty genera altogether, but with the exception of nine rather specialized genera which account for six of the eleven tribes, there are primitive, more well-developed, and highly-developed species within each genus.

The evolution of the *Myrmicinae*, except for the few more dominant genera, is one of major generic jumps and inherent instinctive habits of life. The evolution of the *Formicinae* is largely one of small anatomical changes, some inherent instinctive changes, and immense developments of flexible physiological and behavioural characteristics and facultative as opposed to instinctive behaviour patterns.

The habits of the Harvesting ants and the Leaf-cutting ants are discussed in sections of the chapter devoted to special forms of ant behaviour, and those of the genera *Crematogaster*, *Monomorium*, and *Solenopsis* in the next chapter. Before taking up the third great line of ant evolution, that of the *Dolichoderinae* and *Formicinae*, there is need for some comment on the other twelve Myrmicine tribes, together with a short account of their cousins the *Pseudomyrminae* and their place in the general story. But there are so many peculiar characteristics of anatomy and behaviour that it is impossible to describe them all. For this group of twelve tribes and the *Pseudomyrminae* (about which something must be said because of their status) are truly the *diversa* of the ant world.

For slender beauty and grace of movement *Ocymyrmex* of the African deserts, sole representative of its tribe, is only equalled by *Macromischa* of the *Leptothoracini*. For sheer fantastic development of plated armour the *Melissotarsus* soldier is unrivalled. Each joint of its unbelievably stubby legs is a flattened plate and its body armour is fashioned in proportion. Little use these ants with their small sub-terranean colonies have made of their armour-plated soldiers, unique in being the only known soldier ant to be no larger than the worker, save as super-heavyweight excavating machines which use their armour-plated legs and bodies as living shovels and boring machines. The worker's leg armour is equally remarkable and its general plating not much less than that of the soldier. How they manage to dig is another matter, for their lethargy and slowness of movement is unsurpassed. The swift graceful-moving *Ocymyrmex* is the exact opposite of these primitive slothful creatures. Suspect of being a harvesting ant, *Ocymyrmex* has a special type of desert equipment often encountered in species living amongst sand. Underneath the head there are a quantity of curved hairs pointing both forwards and upwards. Other hairs point downwards and inwards, then upwards again from below the cheeks. These hairs enable the ants to clean their combs *de toilette* on their forelegs when, as frequently happens, they become clogged with sand. Another ant thus equipped belongs to another of the twelve tribes. This is *Pogonomyrmex barbatus* of the *Myrmicini*, the tribe named after the European and North American genus *Myrmica*, the primitive red hunting ants of the garden. The name of *P. barbatus* is another myrmecological (ant!) joke. In mixed Greek and Latin it means 'the bearded beardy ant'. Actually *Pogonomyrmex* is one of the most successful of the genera relegated to the *diversa* and once achieved a temporary fame as the remarkable 'Agricultural Ant' which cleared all the ground round its nests and then at a convenient distance planted, or at least purposely allowed to grow, a fine crop of welcome vegetation, methodically sectioned off by clearly-kept roads.

The Mediterranean *Cardiocondyla* of Tunis and Asia Minor has a wingless male that joins with the workers in the work of the colony. The *Cataulacini* of Central America with the solitary genus *Cataulacus* have fantastic heads, deeply hollowed concavely on top, thus shielding the compound eyes, placed on the rounded sides behind, from any direct vision straight ahead. The whole effect is rather like a squashed-in rubber ball in which a puppy has bitten a hole, with the dented side forming the front and top of the head and the eyes placed behind the rim on the rounded sides. Strangely, the ants seem to need their eyes to see where they are going, making this peculiar structure a most uneconomic provision of nature, for as a result of it they walk forwards obliquely – half forwards and half sideways – and not infrequently find it easier to run backwards in the direction in which their vision is unobstructed.

The links to the *Ponerinae* undoubtedly lie in the *Metaponini* and *Melissatarsini*, especially in the genera *Metapone* (solitary genus of the former tribe) and *Rhopalomastix*, of the latter, solitary cousin genus to the *Melissotarsus* already described, but with a male that is undisputably Ponerine. Indeed, both these genera were for a long time classified as belonging to the *Ponerinae*.

The sub-family *Pseudomyrminae* consists of two genera, *Pseudomyrma* and *Pachysima*. Here for the benefit of other ant students it should be quickly explained that *Pachysima* is the genus *Sima* they knew so well. Unfortunately, it was found that *Sima* was a synonym of an earlier name, *Tetraponera*, and had in consequence to be abandoned, and its sub-generic name *Pachysima* was raised to generic status to represent it in its stead. The *Pseudomyrminae*, long considered as members of the *Promyrmicinae* section of the sub-family *Myrmicinae*, are undoubtedly close relatives of both the Myrmicine and Ponerine sub-families. The petiole of these ants has only one clear knot, the second one being more akin to the first segment of the gaster although much thinner. They are immensely thin for their size – they are often more than a centimetre long – with especially narrow heads. This makes them well adapted for living in the tubular branches and twigs of plants, as is frequently their habit. All the species of the sub-family except one live in shrubs and trees, and not on the ground. The New World *Pseudomyrma* lives most frequently in the thorns of *Acacia*, the plants seeming to flourish the better for their odd tenants and to gain advantage from the protection afforded. This despite the destruction of tissues involved in the original hollowing out of the stem to form the nesting site. Another South American plant, *Triplaris*, of the *Polygonaceae* family, has many hollow stems which are said always to be occupied by ants of this genus. In the Old World the *Pseudomyrminae* are represented by the genus *Pachysima* which have similar habits, with the single exception of the Indian *Pachysima rufonigra*, which is a harvesting ant. The larvae of the *Pseudomyrminae* have a peculiar sac beneath their gullets which is nearly always found to contain a pellet of debris like that of an owl. Usually such pellets are made up of insect debris, but sometimes pollen and plant remains are found. But for the most part these ants are carnivorous. Their grubs also possess a stridulatory (sound-producing) organ, a feature found in no other ant larvae.

While all these phases in the evolution of the other sub-families were in progress the *Ponerinae* continued to develop themselves at a slow rate, and among their eleven tribes and eight sub-tribes a few genera arose which have achieved some measure of success: smaller success it is true than that of any of the higher *Myrmicinae*, but nevertheless noteworthy. Indeed one of the most widespread species of ants in the world to-day is a Ponerine, and by no means a degenerate and despicable one. This is *Odontomachus haematodes*. The colonies of this and other *Odontomachus* are relatively small compared to those of ants of other sub-families: a thousand individuals or thereabouts is about their general best, and a few hundred or even less than a hundred may be nearer the mark in some species. The *Odontomachini* have extraordinary long thin mandibles, which are inserted into the head near the centre of the forward edge, instead of at the two anterior corners. They gain their name of 'Tak' ants from the manner in which they use these peculiar mandibles to propel themselves backwards. Approaching close to a hard rounded object with their mandibles open they snap them together with immense rapidity, catching the edge of the stone in the point of their mandibles. Sliding off the hard surface, the mandibles close completely, and in doing so project the *Odontomachus* backwards a distance of several inches. The ants use this odd method of jumping backwards to escape from their enemies.

The *Odontomachus* are sufficiently virile to have undergone considerable speciation like the higher ants, having many local races. Yet their basic colony behaviour remains rooted in their primitive past. They, like their cousins the *Leptogenyini*, still feed their grubs with unregurgitated food, and the habit of mutual regurgitation between the workers is undeveloped. The *Leptogenyini* are the only other group of Ponerine ants beside the *Odontomachini* and *Myrmecia* (the Bulldog ants) which have colonies of more than a hundred individuals. They are termite-hunting ants from Indian and African tropics and march in well-ordered columns in their expeditions against them. *Leptogenys*, unlike *Odontomachus*, is confined to the tropics, but has many species. It exhibits a primitive trait in the very slight differentiation between queen and worker – in many cases the workers and the worker-like queen are almost indistinguishable except for the latter's distended gaster and its possession of a seminal vesicle and well-developed ovaries.

The evolution of the *Dolichoderinae* from the *Ponerinae* occurred long before *Odontomachus* and *Leptogenys* had proceeded very far in their development of species, but not before the main Ponerine groups and genera were well established. With the solitary exception of the Dolichoderine genus *Aneuretus* (and its fossil cousins *Protaneuretus* and *Paraneuretus*) no living member of the *Dolichoderinae* and their descendants, the *Formicinae*, possesses a sting. In this they differ from all the other sub-families. In the *Dolichoderinae* there is nearly always some rudimentary trace of the degenerate sting, but even this is absent in the *Formicinae*.

Aneuretus simoni is the solitary representative of its genus. It is very rare and is found in Ceylon. A more satisfactory missing link could scarcely be found, for its head, with its small triangulate mandibles, well-developed clypeus and general smooth arrangement, is typically Dolichoderine, while its petiole and sting are typically Ponerine. The normal petiole of the *Dolichoderinae* has a single plate for protection. There is no second joint to the petiole and the gaster is exceptionally mobile, the flattened petiole enabling it to be swung in almost any direction and at many angles. These ants defend themselves by means of the fluid produced from special anal glands. This liquid, which is squirted at their enemies, has an obnoxious odour, and it quickly solidifies into a resin-like consistency. It is most effective in incapacitating even the most powerful enemy ants. The vestigial sting and poison apparatus are similar to that of the *Ponerinae* and *Myrmicinae*, and the orifice at the posterior end of the gaster (an orifice that serves all functions – anal, repugnatorial, etc.) is still slit-form as it is in those subfamilies.

The Dolichoderine ants, with the exception of the *Aneuretini* and their solitary living and two fossil genera, all live in large, highly developed societies. They are long-legged, thinly armoured, swiftly-moving creatures, fond of the sun and at home alike in forest and desert. In the deserts, *Iridomyrmex* has no rival as a swift runner. In the forests, *Azteca* rivals *Pseudomyrma* in its symbiosis with the plants. There are virtually no primitive genera beside *Aneuretus* and the ants of this sub-family are numerous throughout the whole world except in Africa and a few limited localities of the

Ant History

colder regions, such as Great Britain, where its solitary representative is the scavenging *Tapinoma erraticum*. Relationships with other species and other sub-families of ants is something of a speciality of the *Dolichoderinae* and their nests are frequently found near to, or even joined with, those of other ants. In the latter case their brood is always kept separate: the relationship is as it were partnership and not marriage. Usually they benefit from these relationships, either by protection or the scavenging of food, or even its theft. It is this common trait of scavenging that gains them the title of the Scavenger ants. They include one honeypot ant, in which certain workers have the crop so well developed and extensible that they act as honey butts for the rest of the colony. This is *Leptomyrmex rufipes*, from New Guinea and Australia. One Dolichoderine species, *Iridomyrmex sanguineus*, is a great enemy of Termites and is said to occupy 80 per cent of the nests of the common Termites, *Drepanotermes silvestrii*, and *Hamitermes perplexus*, in South Queensland, Australia. Even more famous is the dreaded Argentine Ant, *Iridomyrmex humilis*, which has since the days of steamships spread throughout the world, destroying the native ant fauna in many places. The story of most of the Dolichoderines with their immobile helpless grubs and complex societies is that of the Social Ants, and will be found in the next chapter.

The history of a single sub-family now remains to be traced; this is the *Formicinae*, latest and finest flower of the ant kingdom. Differenced from the *Dolichoderinae* by its possession of a scale on its petiole (it, like the *Dolichoderinae*, has no post-petiole) and by the form of its poison apparatus, it is a descendant of early Dolichoderine stock. The poison apparatus is devoid of all trace of a sting, but is well developed, not atrophied, as in the *Dolichoderinae*, to form a powerful acid-squirting apparatus. The acid secreted is named formic acid, from the Latin *Formica*, an ant, and is nowadays synthesized commercially for industrial purposes. There are no anal repugnatorial glands like those found in the *Dolichoderinae*.

The gizzard of the *Formicinae* is a more complicated structure than that of the other ants – a complexity that is
probably associated with its increased importance in the
greater development of mutual feeding by regurgitation. In
the primitive forms of *Formicinae*, like the *Dimorphomyrmicini*,
this development is incomplete and the relationship of the
complicated twistings of the sepals of the later structure can
thus be clearly traced from that of the Dolichoderine and
Ponerine ancestors.

The appearance of the *Formicinae* and the story of the
growth of their more primitive societies into the highest
forms of ant life marks the beginning of the era of the Social
Ants, the story of which is told in the following chapter.

CHAPTER 3

The Social Ants

*

THE *Formicinae* were born near the birthplace of the first ant, at least within the confines of Central Eurasia. By this time other *Formicidae* were spread far and wide throughout the world, for the first Formicine appeared, as near as can be dated, some thirty to forty million years after the first ant. Its genera were established within the next twenty or thirty million years, but its numerous species have continued to develop in quite modern times and may indeed still be evolving to-day. The *Formicinae* are the only one of the eight sub-families in which it seems likely that evolution is still in progress. One of the most remarkable features of ant evolution is the incredible stability of form that even the species have maintained since early Mesozoic times, after their immense initial burst of evolution and diversification.

But the appearance of the first of the *Formicinae* did not quite usher in the first social ants, by which is meant the first of the complex communities of the higher ants. Although it would appear likely that the highly social communities of the *Camponotini*, *Oecophyllini*, *Acanthomyopsini*, *Formicini*, and *Plagiolepidini* appeared before those of the social *Myrmicinae* (see p. 44), this is by no means certain, and it is likely that the social Dolichoderines were well established before the advent of the later tribes of their cousin offspring. It was in any case some little time before the higher Formicines appeared; not long, it is true, but long enough for the appearance of half a dozen most primitive forms. Some of these primitive forms may have been throwbacks developed coincidentally with, or even later than, the higher forms, but to one or more there indisputably belongs the right to claim the original ancestry of this important group. To them belongs the right to start this tale of the Era of the Social Ants.

As in the other ant groups, these primitive forms must be

sought in the tropics and in the isolated corners of the earth. They, like all the other *Formicinae*, primitive though they are, share the common characteristics of the sub-family. None has a trace of a sting, and the orifice through which it would appear at the end of the gaster, had it been present, is circular and surrounded by a small ring of hairs. In place of the sting they have an acid-squirting apparatus, sometimes poorly developed, but sometimes capable of projecting the fluid to a distance of from eighteen to twenty-four inches. There is a single petiole – no post-petiole – and this is usually surmounted by a scale. Only rarely is a rounded or rumpled knot found.

The primitive *Formicinae* belong to six tribes: the *Myrmecorhynchini* and the *Myrmoteratini*, which share a complete section, the *Heteroformicinae;* the *Dimorphomyrmicini*, the *Santschiellini* and the *Gigantiopini* of the section *Euformicinae*, to which the majority of higher Formicines also belong; and finally the *Melophorini* of the *Alloformicinae*. This last tribe, though primitive, is certainly less justifiably classed as such than the rest, and differs from them not only in its habits – it is a honeypot ant (see pp. 88-90) – but also in having eyes which are rather smaller than the norm. All the other primitive Formicines have immense eyes. Few of them are as large as the fantastic optics of *Santschiella kohli*, of the Belgian Congo, which cover over half the surface of its largish head, but most are large enough to be noteworthy and a handy guide to their classification. *Santschiella*, solitary generic representative of its tribe, like four of the other name-genera of these six tribes, is a tree ant. *Gigantiops*, the leaping Brazilian Formicine, is the most graceful of all the jumping ants. Living on the ground in small colonies of from fifty to sixty individuals, it is frequently found on neighbouring bushes, where it can be seen blithely leaping from leaf to leaf. It jumps like a cat, not quickly and erratically like the Bulldog ants or like *Odontomachus*, but smoothly with a take-off that fits in with the rhythm of its pace. Strangest of all these primitive Formicines is the Burmese *Opisthopis*, large-eyed, thin-bodied, but with a large, broad head, deeply indented behind. It has long, thin, many-toothed mandibles mounted almost centrally, much like those of *Odontomachus*. These fret-saw-like weapons are so long as to surpass the length of the entire thorax.

The *Dimorphomyrmicini*, although possessing only four genera, are sub-divided into two sub-tribes, the *Brachymyrmecini* and the *Dimorphomyrmecini*. The former possesses in its name genus *Brachymyrmex* two ants, *B. cordemoyi* and *B. heeri*, which used to be dominant species of the hothouse fauna throughout the world. Originating in Central and South America, they were carried to Madagascar and to Europe on imported plants and fruit, and in Réunion *B. cordemoyi* was for long the dominant house ant. Both species have now been largely ousted by either *Prenolepis* or *Pheidole*. These ants live in large and well-developed colonies, yet their relatives in the second sub-tribe are exceptionally primitive, including the relic *Gesomyrmex*, first found as fossil in the Baltic amber and only later described alive, when it was found eking out a tenuous primitive existence in Ceylon.

The *Camponotini*, name tribe of the great genus *Camponotus*, contain several primitive genera reminiscent of these earlier forms. Such are the large-eyed *Opisthopis* (surely an inspired name) of Australia, which yet live near-troglodyte lives, thieving from the Termites; *Dendromyrmex*, from Tropical America, another great-eyed ant which builds cotton nests in the branches of trees; the hairy metallic sheened Australian *Calomyrmex*; and the sluggish Indian *Echinopla*, covered with minute cylindrical projections and looking like a cross between a hedgehog and a microscopic edition of a moving Devil's Causeway.

On the whole, however, it is to the species within the genera that we must turn to find the primitive Formicines and follow their evolution. *Camponotus*, the ant student's cross because of its numerous sub-genera and abundance of species, represents the peak of Formicine and Formicid diversity of breeding; while *Polyrhachis*, with its vast array of varied spiny armour, takes the palm for sheer anatomical variety. *Oecophylla* will always take a mention in the pages of the text-books because its workers use their larvae as shuttles to weave the threads that join their nests – the only known example of any insect making use of a tool. *Prenolepis,* small, energetic, and populous, has the widest range, from Antarctica through the tropics to the temperate regions of the North. It can even claim the conquest of the air as the dominant genus of the many ant species found to-day in airplanes, despite the constant spraying and other insecticidal precautions. But it is to *Formica* that we must turn both for the largest societies and for the greatest exhibition of learning ability and plastic behaviour. The vast interconnected communities of the Wood Ants *F. rufa* and *F. exsecta* have been known to have as many as 150 interlinked nests within a single ant nation – a community that represents a conglomeration of twelve million individuals – and colonies of ten to twenty nests (one to two million individuals) are common, while the facultative slave-maker *F. sanguinea* is voted by all ant students to be the species of ant with the greatest mental development. The genus *Formica* is thus the best exemplar for the general story, which can then be extended and embroidered from the larger and more diverse mass of Formicines and later related to the societies of Dolichoderines and the higher Myrmicines and so to the background of the whole *Formicidae.*

The genus *Formica* contains nearly 200 species and subspecies which have been divided at different times into a variety of different arrangements of groups and sub-genera, and for that matter of varieties, races, and other often unnecessary sub-special divisions. The picture of the evolution of the 'grand societies' remains unaffected by such taxonomic arguments and factions. It is a picture clearly seen by the study of forms ranging from the primitive *F. fusca* type of *Formica* to those of *F. rufa* and *F. exsecta,* on the one hand, and *F. sanguinea* on the other.

The Large Black ant (*F. fusca*) is common throughout North America, the whole of Northern Europe and Asia, and Japan. When found in more southern regions, as near the Mediterranean, it is a mountain ant, often being found at great heights. Slimly built and dull black in colour, though often with a more or less reddish thorax, it is about one-fifth to three-tenths of an inch long, the queens being somewhat larger (about two-fifths) and generally more robust. The males are usually slightly larger than the largest workers. Standing high on its legs, *F. fusca* moves at a quick pace when out foraging, although since it usually proceeds by a series of quick short bursts, its overall speed over largish distances may be comparatively low and of the order of about two feet per minute. The nests of *fusca* are simple structures excavated in the earth either under stones or heathland, or also surmounted by a small solarium made of earth and growing grass, or bits of heather, gorse, or twigs, according to what materials are handy. The true nest is always in the earth, the solarium when present being the summer sun-trap, inhabited only during the warm summer months, and then usually only in the daytime. The numbers in the colony may be small – 200 to 300 workers and two or three queens – or it may consist of three or four thousand individuals with a larger number of queens. *F. fusca* nests are rarely permanent, being frequently moved from one site to another, not merely seasonally, but often several times throughout the year. Occasionally permanent nests of several years' duration are established in a favourable site, but this is the exception, not the rule. The nests themselves are simple in structure, consisting of relatively few largish chambers and surrounding passages. They rarely extend for more than eight or nine inches into the earth, usually six or seven inches, and the mounds when they occur are only from five to seven inches in height and from six to nine inches in diameter. Large numbers of *fusca* nests may occur in a small area, but they are never linked together by communal tracks, as in the higher *Formicas*. Each nest is a simple self-contained unit. They live by hunting for prey (other insects) and by milking stray aphids or coccids, which they find on the trees or bushes near their nests. In foraging for these foods, individual ants will often travel eight or ten yards from the nest, though rarely further, except to climb trees, the tallest of which they will ascend to great heights if they are found within the hunting range. All foraging is an individual matter undertaken by isolated ants, who may, however, set out more or less together and forage in the same district, meeting, seemingly by accident, at short intervals and then setting off anew in opposite directions. During these expeditions the *fusca* will frequently wander on to the tracks of other ants, even foraging on the less frequented branches of a tree virtually possessed by another more populous species. If intercepted by the 'owners' they are pacific, remain motionless, except for their gently waving feelers, and are usually accepted as at least non-hostile intruders if not individuals there by right. The other species get used to these incursions, and since the *fusca* rarely go beyond the limit of their tolerance, leaving the carefully pastured aphid and coccid herds alone, and seeking only the strays or much neglected ones, they do not interfere with them. *F. fusca* do not keep aphid herds of their own, either within or outside the nest, although, despite the small size of their communities, more than seventy-three species of ant guests have been found within their nests.

Thus their habits are simple and in general primitive, but they possess at the same time all the attributes of the *Formicinae*. Their grubs are naked, immobile, and completely dependent on the worker's care and attention. Reciprocal regurgitation both between grubs and workers and between the workers themselves is highly developed. The behaviour of individual ants is by no means primitive and experiments by the author using mazes for testing their learning ability show that there is considerable variation in this ability among individuals. The general order of competence in learning simple mazes is far superior to that of Myrmicine ants like *Myrmica*, which have a comparably primitive mode of life. Their behaviour in experimental plaster of paris arenas designed to aid in the investigation of 'the division of labour' is also markedly different. When *Myrmica* ants are released from their nesting-place and allowed to enter the arena containing different types of food sources, all the

workers rush out at once in a body and pour into the arena.
No workers stay behind with the queens, which may themselves leave the nest. This mass of ants swarms all over the
area, individually wandering from food source to food
source, and eventually returning to the nest. Only after a
long period of such scrimmaging is any trail between food
sources and the nest set up. In the case of *F. fusca*, however,
the picture is very different. On the opening of the nest entrance, releasing the ants, a single ant, or at most one or
two, will leave the nest. The first venture is only a brief incursion into the area immediately surrounding the entrance
and a hurried return. Twenty or thirty seconds later the
same individual ant, or ants, will make another sortie attended this time by two or three companions, and a more
thorough examination of the area is undertaken. The food
sources – the honey, aphids feeding on a small shoot, grass
and other materials placed there to encourage a diversity
of activities – are soon discovered and the explorers return
once more to the nest. Before doing so they may partly fill
their crops with honey-dew from the aphides, or with honey,
but never completely fill them – the work of the colony, it
would seem, must first be set in order. Within a minute or
two of their return to the nest, the work commences. The
explorers lead off along the routes to the various centres
which they discovered and other workers follow them,
searching round a bit perhaps on arrival before settling to
their labours, but not for long. Within five or ten minutes
of the first sortie, regular trails are in existence to each centre
and the flow of work is fully established. Sometimes just before the final setting up of the trails there is a brief sortie of
large numbers of individuals (never of all of them), but this
is soon over and the division of the labour of the colony is
established. Furthermore, when different occupations are
provided, it will be found that certain of the individuals in
the colony tend initially to investigate certain ones more
frequently than others, and to commence future occupations
connected with them more quickly than the other ants. This
is a reflection of their past learning – of their memory of past

jobs of the same type. These 'leaders' of the first sortie and their later companions and ants with evident memories are the 'excitement centre' ants (see p. 10 *et seq.*). In the maze experiments it is they who are found to have the most highly developed learning ability in any particular community. This variation in the ability to learn not only mazes, convenient tools of the laboratory, but also the doing of actual tasks, is markedly less amongst the individuals of the average *Myrmica* colony. Excitement centre activity is also comparably less in evidence.

Formica fusca may be a primitive hunter which lives in small communities, but it is far from being a primitive ant. It is an example of the general rule that distinguishes the *Formicinae* and, to a lesser extent, the *Dolichoderinae*, from the other ants, that the primitiveness is no longer a matter of archaic as opposed to newer types of genera and species. It is a more refined difference, little connected with anatomical form or gross differences in instinctive patterns of life. It is the difference between simplicity and complexity of ways of life, similar to the difference between the life of tribal man and civilized man. Such human comparisons are always dangerous and the study of ants has suffered much from their too frequent use, but here, within this limited sphere, the simile is useful in illustrating and defining the type of difference which is meant. It is wrong and very much to be regretted when, as too often occurs even in more serious books on ants, such phrases as the primitive hunters, the pastoral communities, the rise of the city, and fascism or communism, are used with human connotations in reference to the evolution of ant behaviour. Such similes have in any case no strict relevance except within the confines of a single genus of fixed basic potential, and should then only be used, and that most sparingly, to indicate a general type of event. There is no direct comparison. There is with ants, of course, no question of Fascism or Communism, nor for that matter of Automatonism. The best way of interpreting ant societies is to do so in terms of ant behaviour. The increase of the size of the ant community necessitates a correlated increase of food supply and, for that matter, of security of supply. The increase of the food supply of a Formicine community leads to an increase in territory. These are the phenomena and elementary social and economic factors whose evolution and mechanisms must now be traced.

The simple *fusca* colonies show one as yet unmentioned development of some interest. The queens are, as has been said, noticeably, yet not vastly, larger than the workers, and are present in small numbers in the nest, numbers which vary from two or three in a small colony of 200 or 300 workers, to five or six in colonies of 900 to a thousand. This proportion of queens to workers is relatively high and, though in *F. fusca* it lessens with increasing population, it is maintained as a general rule amongst the large communities of *F. rufa*, *F. exsecta*, and their kindred, as well as in the less populous colonies of *F. sanguinea*, where a general average of a queen per thousand workers is maintained. This re-splitting of the fertility to a larger degree than is found in the majority of ants has brought both good and bad effects. It has brought a greater stability of survival. Extreme limitation of fertility to a single individual, a rare event in the normal ant society, leads to dangerous vulnerability. If the queen is destroyed, the colony must find another fertilized queen at the next marriage flight, or be able to substitute a fertile worker in her place. In a large society this latter is impossible, since if it were single-queened, the queen would of necessity be a much larger individual than the workers in order to be able to lay the vast numbers of eggs needed to produce her numerous offspring. The size difference between worker and queens would be great, as in *Pheidole*, *Tetramorium*, or most of all *Carebara*, and even *Pheidole* and *Tetramorium* normally have several queens. In the case of a species having workers as large as *F. rufa* or *F. sanguinea*, such a queen would be a monstrous unwieldy giant. When the size difference is so great, worker substitution for queens, the occurrence of so-called gynacoid workers, is rare. It would almost seem that extreme concentration of fertility with the production of vast numbers of eggs by two or three individuals leads to extreme sterility of the degenerate female worker caste.

The return towards a greater spreading of fertility does not in fact mean a comparable lessening of the fertility of each individual queen. The *Formica* queen may not produce the same number of offspring as a *Pheidole* queen, and she certainly does not produce the 30,000 eggs each seven weeks that the *Eciton* queen produces, but she does produce a goodly number.

The occurrence of the queens in *F. fusca* has led to little further development. The ill-protected colonies do indeed have greater security and when they become large there is a tendency for a splitting off of one or more queens with groups of workers to form new colonies nearby. These remain distinct new colonies, rapidly developing their own particular colony badge, and cease to have any connexion with the mother colony from which they sprang. The queens of *F. fusca* are quite capable of founding colonies on their own, and normally start their nests in this manner, a thing beyond the ability of many *Formica* queens.

The revolution from this simple life started with the settling down of the *Formicas* to build simple but permanent nests, as do many of *F. fusca*'s close relatives (such as *F. subsericea*, *F. neocinera* and *F. lecontei* of North America and *F. rufibarbis* and *F. picea* of Britain and the rest of Europe) and the beginning of the establishment of definite hunting areas and aphid-milking places. Sureness of food supply for a permanent colony rapidly began, in this now generalized story, to come to mean regular food-getting habits and the gradual definition of territory. It was no good the ants going to definite areas to forage and to milk aphides if other ants from other colonies of the same species, or from other species, also habitually gathered their food from these same places. The places must be owned by the colony, farmed and foraged over only by them. This in turn entailed a growth of group-foraging along trails leading to and from the feeding areas and the nest. New areas could still be sought by individuals and, if worthy of it, incorporated into the territory of the colony, but the original territory must be adequately covered, foraged over, and, moreover, protected.

The establishment of territory brought other events with it. The area nearest the nest is not necessarily entirely dominated: territory is not necessarily a matter of concentric areas of strong, weaker, and only partial domination, spreading outwards from the nest. This is found, typically in the subterranean aphid-farming *Acanthomyops* such as *A. mixtus*, but it is rarely the case in the light-loving and ubiquitous feeding *Formicas*. Territory spreads out in strips, wedges, and sometimes in slim tongues, with vast expansions at their outer limits. Territory is a matter of the history of the individual community and of the variable economic importance of the different areas. But one thing is certain, hostile *competing* nests of the same or other species of ants will not be allowed in the immediate vicinity of the nest. The splitting off of colonies now presents itself differently. Times and habits have changed. Areas are dominated and owned, and roads lead to and fro throughout the countryside. Nearby colonies of the same species, whether split off or established independently by other queens, would mean haphazard distribution of nests unrelated to the economic potentiality of the various localities of the area. The district might in fact be able to support a number of large nests of ants of the species if they were properly distributed throughout it, but placed haphazard, probably mainly grouped close together in relatively small parts of the area, they would compete for territory with bloody warfare and widespread destruction. Whole nests would be wiped out and the survivors weakened; events of ill-omen for the survival of the species itself. That this does not happen is due to other coincident changes. The mode of nest foundation is now no longer that of the solitary or shared ordeal of one or more queens struggling to survive until their brood are hatched mature from the cocoons to help them, care for them, and feed them. The colonies are founded by the habitual establishment of this splitting off of one or two queens (rarely single ones) with a few workers, who set up home in a new part of the area just outside the lands of the colony territory. The new nest is joined to the mother nest by a new road along which willing helpers scurry, and if the new nest survives the colonial territory is extended. All this while there has been a steady increase in the population of the individual nests. The coming of the territorial phase meant more as well as securer food.

This foundation of new colonies by means of splitting off of groups of queens accompanied by workers soon led to the development of a dependence on help in colony foundation on the part of the queens. Few of the large colonial *Formicas* have queens capable of founding their colonies unaided, a factor which was to have wider implications than are immediately apparent. The growth of these communes was at first limited to some half a dozen, or at most a dozen, settlements of ten or twenty thousand individuals apiece. As the population of each nest increased with the success of the communes in competition with non-communal forms, so new kinds appeared with greater fertility and greater adaptability to communal life.

There is, of course, one essential of any community, and especially of those claiming and exercising territorial ownership and rights. Both individuals and territory must be recognizable. There must be some badge, whether intentional or resulting from some inherent habit or characteristic, which defines the individual as belonging to one commune or solitary settlement, or another. Moreover, some element of this distinction must also be established in relation to the territory. The ants have such badges. The badge of each ant colony, each nest or settlement, is its odour. Each ants' nest of every species has a more or less well-developed nest odour. There is some special discussion of the ants' senses in Chapter 5; here it will suffice to say that the most highly developed sense in every ant is its sense of smell. Some ants have well-developed eyes; others are blind. All have, compared to our primitive conception of it, an exceptionally well-developed sense of smell. Just as our prime sense is that of sight, so that of the ants is smell.

There is no reason to believe, as will be later seen, that the ants' sense of smell is in any way fundamentally different from ours: it is just developed to a degree that we poor mortals, who can only say that a thing smells 'like' or 'of' something else, find difficult to comprehend. The ants can no doubt recognize some hundreds of different smells, but not many thousands.

Each nest of ants the world over cannot therefore be supposed to have a unique odour, exceptional to itself. The matter is much simpler. In the thorax of the ants there are a small group of glands called the metathoracic glands. These glands produce a liquid which is expressed through small tubes on to the cuticle, or outer skin of the ant, and the liquid thus expressed on to the surface of the body smells. This liquid provides only the basic constituent of the nest odour. It provides a liquid which smells slightly different in most species – a difference in odour that is only appreciable by the human nose in a few species, such as *Acanthomyops fuliginosus*, the Jet Black Ant of Europe and North America, or the Stink Ant *Paltothyreus tarsatus* of southern Africa. The acid-squirting *Formicinae* tend to smell of formic acid, but most ants seem to us humans to have little smell unless they are crushed, and may even then not produce any distinctive odour, or even any appreciable odour at all. Yet to other ants they smell. This species odour may be strongly or weakly developed. In species of ants like *Leptothorax acervorum*, *L. emersoni*, and *Formicoxenus nitidulus*, which often live almost entirely as guests in the nests of other quite unrelated species of ants, experiments indicate that the smell is poorly developed, if not entirely absent. They smell, as befits their way of life, neutral!

There is also strong evidence that, as might be suspected, this odour is similar in related species of ants, although rarely completely identical. The nest odour is formed quite simply by the influence of the ants' lives upon this basic odour. The extreme development of the mutual licking of one ant by another within the large nests and communes of the social ants ensures the even spreading of the slightest deviation. In species where this habit is less in evidence, and these are always species living in small societies, the evenness of spreading is less effective. This results in the species odour being more important as being the common bond, and a subsequent greater facility of acceptance of members of the same species as friends and not as enemies. Thus different colonies of *Myrmica*, *Ponera*, and their like will usually join together and unify when placed together in captivity. Only the settlement of the brood and queens, the more frequently licked elements, will cause trouble. This is fitting, for the competition of the primitive Ponerines and Myrmicines is an inter-species competition, while that of the social ants is often inter-communal, or at least between very closely related species which have similar economic needs.

The licking causes trouble in the case of both the queens and brood of the *Myrmicas* and in the communes and nests of the social ants, because it spreads the differential qualities that go to alter the crude smell of the metathoracic fluid (the species odour), turning it into a distinctive communal badge. The materials of the nest, the numerous guests inside the nest (many of which are also constantly licked by the ants), the different types and mixtures of food eaten and even the different types of debris, like carrion, met with near or in the nests, or within the territory (within which carrion will not be tolerated), all provide elements that, through the constant contact of ants' mouths and bodies, go to flavour the species odour. The constant licking spreads these elements throughout the colony, and pupae, naked or in cocoons, and newly hatched adult ants do not have this odour. Throw them together in a box and they will form an equally well-defined community unit of their own, even if their origins spring from a hundred different nests or communes. Even different species will mix happily for a while in this state, showing that the species odour itself is slow to develop. In the end, such mixed colonies formed of a variety of different species of young ants and cocoons will nearly always break up in fighting as the metathoracic fluid is produced more adequately, but this is not always the case since familiarity and constant intermingling may cause habituation and acceptance. If the ants' antennae, which are their noses, are covered with wax, they are in effect blinded and are unable to recognize either friend or foe. In such cases they often, in their fear, tend to attack all other living creatures, but after a while become more calm and will happily mix with quite foreign species. In the same way a war of ants can be stopped by the enforced masking of badges brought about by the overpowering of their nest and species odour by a more powerful one, such as cau-de-cologne.

The nest odour is thus the badge of the ants, but it is a natural badge that does not debar familiarity with other badges and their peace-time acceptance. A large commune of wood ants, *Formica rufa*, of some sixteen to twenty nests, or even a single-nested settlement of Jet Ants (*Acanthomyops fuliginosus*) will have many contacts with other species of ants in their territory. At the borderland fringes other ants will wander solitary or in groups according to their wont, often invading the more tightly held hinterland. These other ants will not in peacetime be attacked unless they themselves are hostile, or invade the treasured herding grounds, try to steal prey already attacked, or found by the wood or jet ants, or approach too close to the nests. The Jet Ant (*Ac. fuliginosus*) is also a woodland ant and may often be found nesting within the confines of *F. rufa* territory. When this happens, there is no sharing of trails or of hunting-grounds. The jet ants have their territory and the wood ants do not invade it, for although a peaceful ant the jet ant is strong and is rarely attacked because of its especial odour, which is apparently repugnant to other ants. This odour is only partly metathoracic, and is partly produced by special glands within the head. On the trails both of the wood ants and of the jet ants, *F. fusca*, *Myrmica*, and other solitary foragers may be found. In the case of the wood ants, these other species may even nest within their territory. As long as they do not dispute a capture with the wood ants (or jet ants), do not respond pugnaciously when saluted, and do not in fact compete with them for space or food, they are tolerated. It is, however, only such non-competitive species which will be permitted to survive. Woe betide the wood ants of another commune found on the trails, or a stranger *Camponotus* or *Acanthomyops*; they will have short shrift. The resemblance of these foreign but familiar odours can be shown experimentally in captive colonies. It is indeed possible to mix quite happily a number of normally warlike species of ants by a commonsense understanding of these factors. For example, the Jet Ant is peaceable, yet feared; moreover, as can be seen when it is found living in joint communities with the Yellow Lawn Ant, *Acanthomyops mixtus*, as frequently happens, its own strong odour is easily spread over to another species. Taking, then, a base of adult Jet Ants and gradually mixing with them ants of species not unfamiliar with its other odours, a truly poly-odorous ant community can in time be born. Communities of no fewer than eight species have been happily welded together in this fashion by the author. They live at peace and share the labours of the nest one with another over many months. Such situations involving only two species are indeed often found in nature. Perhaps the most extraordinary instance of this, cited now because it demonstrates so clearly the working of the nest odour, is that of the slave-making ants and their slaves. The slave ants are acquired by the slave-making species when still at the pupal stage. When they hatch out they therefore naturally accept the odour of their masters. Their odour on developing plays its own part in altering the odour of the joint community. They recognize neither their own home nest's odour, nor that which would exist had their masters lived without slaves. They will thus quite happily return to the nest of their birth and help their 'masters' to pillage it for more cocoons, and they frequently do this.

Another point about the nest odour is its lack of constancy. Each new element brought within the life and ken of the commune affects it. Individual ants or groups of ants separated from the community for a space of even a few weeks will not at first accept their nest-mates on their return, nor be accepted by them, both because of their own changed nest odour and because that of the community as a whole has changed during their absence. Common types of food, and common types of nest surroundings such as those of plaster of Paris observation nests and similar devices for breeding in captivity, can lead to a lessening of nest-odour distinctions, though not (except through diet) of the basic species odour.

The badge of territory in ants is not equivalent to the badge of individual recognition. It is to a large degree psychological – the badge of habit – and physical – the badge of occupation. Year after year the same roads are worn, the same trees visited, and the same rotting logs are searched for beetles and other prey. There is a difference here between two large groups of ants, those which find their way by sight and those which find their way by smell. Without exception the ants of the large communes find their way by sight, but there are many social ants whose nations are usually single-nested or consist of at most two or three linked settlements, who find their way largely by smell. To this group belong a few of the *Acanthomyops*, and probably Myrmicines as *Pheidole* and *Solenopsis*. These ants leave trails of anal chemical on their routes which they can recognize as their own. Their territory is thus clearly marked in a kindred manner to the individual kinship badge.

The mass of Formicines and Dolichoderines find their way by means of sight with remarkable efficiency. They are less able to follow trails of scent and do not bother to attempt methodically to leave them. Yet their very passage leaves some odour, if only of formic acid, and there is no doubt the major pathways and hunting areas do get marked in this way. The marking is not, however, specific to a nest, but rather to a species. Near the nest it will be strongly marked and further away less so, and a stranger wood ant coming on a strongly-smelling track far away from its nest will immediately start at the defensive. It is as though it realizes this could not lead to its own home.

The marking of wood ant territory is by occupation in full season and by memory, leading the ants out to its farthermost limits at the commencement of the season.

One point about this system still requires some explanation. Two million ants, let alone ten million, cannot each lick all the other members of their vast commune. Furthermore, such vast communes must spread over considerable areas and have individual nests built in a variety of different types of ground and situations. How can they smell the same? The answer is, they don't. It is a matter of gradations and of wideness of familiarity and tolerance. It is a mistake to assume that because ants recognize one another by their nest odours and have a badge which signifies that they belong to a certain community, they are narrow-minded about it. Experience and tolerance play a more important part. The ant accepts what he meets in going about his peaceful avocations as being the *status quo*. Small communities show little tolerance of even the most peaceful intruder because they are more tightly knit together, unused to distant peaceful travel and the meeting of cousins on their routes. The mother colony of these big wood ant communes provides indeed a central nest odour, but one that would not be recognized by a young ant from the communes farthest away, as yet inexperienced in travel. The nest odour of his own particular nest would have some elements of this odour through the contact of its inmates with those of the mother colony. Some of these inmates may have even travelled to the mother colony on a few rare occasions, but the main elements of the nest odour of their distant ant host will be local and therefore different ones. In between this outpost nest and the mother nest there will be other settlements, each with its special qualities of odour, but each influenced by the contact with their neighbour nests and with the mother nest and the outpost colony. The system is one of gradations of nest odour, the variations which in fact mark the members of each settlement of the commune as having a definite home in such and such a nest – at least not in ours, if you please. The 'not in ours' is not so effectively enforced amongst neighbours, but would seem to be *de rigueur* between the most distant settlements if visited *in quantity*. A single ant from the mother nest will in general be accepted at first perhaps with some slight puzzlement, but eventually quite amicably, as long as it enters as if by right without itself showing too much doubt or nervousness. If, as really frightened ants do, it shows hostility, it is lost and attack is certain. A group of twenty or thirty ants will be unlikely to receive the same acceptance and eventual welcome. They would be in danger of constituting a foreign invasion and would therefore be more prone to hostility because of their greater strength.

Hostility is the sign of war: appearance of sudden numbers of ants not recognized as habitués at a feeding site; hunger leading to ferocity; and excessive excitement due to unusual events such as undue heat, can all lead to warfare. In order to survive, the most widespread communes need peace and an adequate food supply. Theoretically there is no limit to the spread of such communes of many settlements of *Formicas*. In practice the largest of them is in danger of upset in emergency owing to the very grave differences in nest odours existing between the outermost regions at either end of the territory. This is especially the case when the mother colony does not continue to increase in size and splendour of population in relation to the number of daughter settlements and the extent of their territory and fails to provide the largest flow of elements towards all the graded nest odours. There is similar danger when the mother colony is not centrally placed. Smaller communes, being more tightly knit and with greater interchange of travellers, are far less liable to the danger of disintegration.

The dependence of these vast communes on the memory of a small proportion of the individual worker ants for the renewal of their interlinking and the re-occupation of their vast territories is even greater than in the case of smaller ant colonies. Each autumn the flow of traffic along the trails slows down and eventually ceases. For a while the foraging still continues in districts near to each individual nest, and for a little longer the guards continue to keep a daily watch on the entrance gates to the ant-hills. As the frosts become more regular, even these lethargic sentinels are withdrawn and only weakened stragglers remain in the depths of the heap. Throughout the winter the ants sleep, safe within the depths of their earthen fortresses.

Wood ant-heaps are nearly always built around some up-right object, most usually a tree stump, though sometimes round a living tree or bush. These mounds of twigs or pine needles are always carefully thatched and drained. In the winter the inside will be found to have remained quite dry even after the wettest weather, and after the destruction of the thatch the lower excavated nest is so adequately drained that the ants are unaffected by damage to the upper part of their mansion. In searching for the ants the construction of their nest is exposed. Immediately below the vast heap, which in the case of an old colony may be five or six feet high, and ten or twelve feet in diameter, are the founda-tions, a large concave pit filled with a mixture of mound materials and earth. Deep below this well-marked hollow there lies the real nest of the ants, their winter home. Channels of clearly excavated earth run slanting sideways and downwards along the lines of roots and other subter-ranean guides for distances of one, two, and three feet. As they are cleared the sleeping ants are found; vast clusters of several thousand individuals each, slowly moving in-wards and outwards to and from the centre of the mass through living passages formed within the tightly clinging bundles. Thus is an equal warmth maintained and death and disease prevented. No ant stays outermost for long and no inside one can steal too great a share of warmth. Only the queens remain always deep inside these living nests, each large cluster containing two, three, or more queens apiece. The queens remain more active, perhaps because of their greater stamina, perhaps because of their greater share of warmth, and even in the coldest weather retain some power of movement and ability to escape. Some workers also remain more active than others. As soon as spring brings returning warmth the queens and these workers begin to stir and move out from amongst their still sleeping colleagues, awaking them in the process. The life of the New Year has begun. At first the dome remains unoccupied. A few workers set out from the lowest doorways in search of food. More come out to sun themselves in close-shouldered ranks on the sunny slopes of the upper nest. Their movements are as yet slow and none too steady. Food is the first essential of the newly-awakened nest and the first to set to work are the job-starters – those inevitable individuals, the excitement centres. In the early days even they remain near the nest, their movements are less elastic and their contacts with the other ants less animated and their stimulation consequently less viable. In a few days, if the cold has not returned, the reawakening is complete, and though energy remains at a low ebb, the pangs of hunger drive the hardier individuals out to the trails. Food must be found. The awakening ants find such food easily, for even the nearest ground, turf, tufts of grass, ling or heather, shrubs and trees, are newly stocked with prey. Tasty morsels may even be found in the long-neglected dome itself. Food comes in in abundance during the first week and many workers can be spared for the all too necessary renovations of the summer nest. Gradually the home ground is cleared of food and the trails push outwards. Already the pattern of memory is being jogged. Each journey outwards re-establishes another link in the chain which will eventually build the whole. It is a slow process by human standards, this progressive awakening of the ant mind to memories of the previous year. Yet it is an individual process dependent on the minute grey cells found even within the humble brain of the ant. The end of each journey outwards brings a reawakening of the memories of the next stage of the nearby food source under a log, or the aphid pastures on the third and fourth branch of a tree. The havering process is begun : short explorations forwards and a return to the known base at the end of the previous chain. A further journeying and another return. The full link may not be re-established until the next journey outwards on the following day, but there is little question of its eventual return. The first parts of the chain return most easily and often the end parts of the links, or even of the whole chain, seem also well remembered, but many a hesitation will guide the puzzled ant through the middle of its course.

As the roads go outwards so the nests are drawn anew nearer together towards their pristine wholeness. The settlements spread outwards like fingered stars. Small ones with shallower nests wake quicker and are often moving first, but larger nests have greater needs and so drive farther and faster once they start. Each nest is at work re-starting the life forgotten during the winter sleep. The dead are cast out, for many have paid the toll of life during the hardness of the frosts, especially during the early days of autumn's coming, before winter can truly be said to have arrived. Once deep down in the earthy depths few die, but many a mouldering corpse will be found within the heap before the warm sun of later March and April has reached the sunken hordes below.

The first meetings between the settlements are those of the job-starters, and are as hesitant as their movements in reforming the most ill-remembered links of memory's chain. They meet startled, and recoil with war-like threatening, but, unsure, seem almost diffident in their ferocity. Eventually one moves on along its trail, pulled by the memory of its onward course. The other turns, retracing its steps to follow it, holding its jaws wide and snapping tentatively at its mid and hindmost legs. The onward-moving ant turns to snap back, causing the follower momentarily to withdraw, then it hurries on. The other ant still follows, still snaps and seizes hold, lets go and moves again in pursuit, but the spirit of war is dying and maybe that of memory stirs. At any rate the fretsome tugging dies, the onward ant moves in peace, and the pursuer turns to renew its own outward course. The picture is repeated with all those early meetings as the excitement centre explorers move outward along the trails encountering anew more commune members from other nests as memory urges them further and further onwards along the trails. The return is an easier passage – still some scurrying but less of it. The earlier meeting has brought results and the urge to homing trail dampens the spirit of delay. On the next day others come from each side, but struggles are less, for the pioneers are learning anew their familiarity and each in turn had taken some smell element of it back with her as a contact odour on the previous day, to arouse the latent memories and familiarities of others. Every meeting condoned by physical contacts such as those of the pioneers (or even fighting in times of real warfare) brings some spreading and mingling of the odours of each ant involved.

Without the survival of this memory of the trail and hunting places, the individual settlements would not be rejoined after their winter segregation, nor would the quick opening up of habitual haunts by each nest individually and by the commune collectively be possible. Many areas would, of course, be re-discovered annually by random exploration commenced *de nouveau*, but many special points of habitual visit would be lost. The settlements also would each year be re-discovered, since each one must be well within the foraging range of its neighbour. No inter-settlement traffic would ever ensue if the settlements were distanced apart at ranges above that of normal wood-ant travel. But such contact would be slower and more dangerous if there was not the drive of memory of the trail to force the pattern of behaviour of the first-met scouts. It is the see-saw passage along a well-fixed channel, more clearly established with each thrust farther forward before return, that forces the rebuilding of familiarity with the equally hesitant scouts from the next nest. Then contact through mixing of the odours of the nest together brings renewed joint acceptance of the mutual membership of the re-connected commune. It is perhaps because little odour can survive along the wintry trails until the coming spring, that no kind of ant which finds its way solely by following such trails forms communes. On the other hand, such ants, like the Doryline armies, will follow trails of other colonies (or their own), or even those of other species if not too distantly related, that are many weeks old.

It would seem that species like the Jet ant (*Acanthomyops fuliginosus*), which are almost entirely dependent on odour trails for finding their way, do have other memories which help them to re-establish their foraging areas after the winter's sleep. They cannot, like the wood ants, re-establish their trails by remembering direction, but they, like most social ants, do have a sense of distance travelled, although whether or not this involves an appreciation of upward and downward movement, as when climbing trees, as a distinct method of travel from ordinary journeying over the ground, is not known. There is no question that the annual re-establishment of their habitual trails is accompanied by a lengthy searching at long distances from the nest into areas which are never re-visited once the trails are re-found, and it may be that it is largely dependent on renewed search each year. It seems more likely, however, that the distance to the trees on which trails were formed may be remembered, and even some of the vertical topography of the route. Once visited, the trail is marked by the job-starters, and can then be followed not only by these individuals, but also by other members of the colony. This is the one advantage of the scent trail – the stimulus of the homeward-coming ant is sufficient to send out another forager to the same spot. All the second forager has to do is to follow the trail of the first one ; it does not have to learn the way by itself, following the first visitor on its return.

The importance of the excitement centre individuals in all the complex activity involved in the re-awakening of the colonies and the re-establishment of the commune can be demonstrated by their removal. The success of any colony of social ants follows the same course when this is done. The economy is immediately affected, for food sources are not all remembered by the remaining workers. Secondary excitement centre ants develop and to some degree replace the earlier ones, often after a space of time with considerable efficiency, but unless some remain who remember the sites and trails, their re-establishment will depend on the energy and initiative of these new élite. If they in turn be removed, then real trouble occurs. The removal of the secondary excitement centres can usually be undertaken at the same time as the removal of those of the first rank, since the secondary ones are the usual companions of the first group, and the quickest of the ruck to respond to their activities. Such an extirpation of 'leaders' is a catastrophe that cannot be overcome during many months and the colony becomes uneconomic and quickly decreases in both territory and population. It may even be so weakened as to fall a prey to the attack of other colonies of the same or different species.

The establishment of the food supply and the renovation of the nest must be speedily achieved at the beginning of each season so that the large spring brood may be housed and fed so well that they develop quickly. They are badly needed to replace the ranks of the winter dead and to make the best use of the full flush of hunting in late May and June.

In the communes the excitement centres play double rôles – once familiarity is regained, they function as communal job-starters at places where the workers mix. But each ant takes the food it gains back to its own nest. There is greater efficiency of food-getting and greater coverage of territory, but apart from the mutual regurgitation of food upon the trails (as frequent as in any single colony of ants), there is no sharing of the booty gained.

The breakdown of these vast communes has been mentioned, but inadequately explained. This must be remedied before the habits of the social ants are linked throughout the groups and the tale is led on in the next chapter to the even stranger stories of the special soldier castes and of the joint societies of different species of ants.

The breakdown of the large ant commune soon develops

once fighting starts. It needs only two irascible individuals to start the war. Once they begin to fight, others are affected by the feel of battle, and join in, making warlike moves at others, which, if taken with equal measure in return, set the woodland scene aflame. One stranger from a distant end of the commune meeting another ant near a mid-point between two further nests can set the tinder flaring. The return to the limited nationality of the settlement is stimulated. Excited reserves come up from both the neighbouring colonies and the war is on. The alarm spreads to other nearby nests whose workers also hurry out and join the fray. At some points in each region of the larger communes there are weaker links where less successful settlements keep the trails less populous and contact is less strong. These points usually form the dividing lines along which the battle spreads and rages. Tens of thousands of ants may fight till dusk – rarely with complete success on either side. The excitement often causes other ruptures far away, for the excitement of battle leads to widespread tetchiness throughout the commune's length, and other distant battles, quite separate from this first one, may start. By nightfall thousands will die, or be dying, and on the morrow the great community is no longer joined. Those who gained territory remove the dead, eating the edible parts and rejecting the hard head, thorax, and the skeleton of the gaster and the legs. For weeks the area of the front is heavily patrolled on either side and a gap in hunting territory is maintained with individual battles where it is broken. The commune is now divided, and only rarely is it re-united. There is all the up-and-down rivalry of differing communities in future years – a rivalry that usually leads either to the decline of one part and the increase of the other, or else a divergence of areas occupied, until with the abandonment of the nearest settlements on either side, the gap is widened and proximity is no longer a danger.

The actual break-up of such communes leading to the isolation of one outlying part (or even of two or three outlying parts) to form a distinct new group of settlements, always depends on such chance developments. Thundery weather, for example, is another frequent accompaniment, for ants respond to it with startling sensitivity, tending to become excited and often dangerously tetchy. The causes are more fundamental. Nearly always they are economic. Isolated nests or groups of nests well within the commune bounds never break away in this fashion. The nests affected are always in outlying parts. Nearer to virgin territory, they expand rapidly with the abundance of food. Populations increase and the outward exploration continues. The linking colonies are comparably weaker – their poorer resources are made still poorer by the competition of their growing neighbours. Their population consequently sinks with their lesser success and a new centre with its pivot away from the central area of the commune is established. The time is ripe for trouble as the dominance increases, and usually it comes. Evenness of population is the only sure preventive against these eventual disruptions, and this only happens if the territory is adjusted as each individual nest grows. This is done by emigration of the kind already mentioned (p. 12), when excitement centres start the struggle away from well-foraged territory to a more economic and more profitable area. (See also pp. 165–7.)

The pathways joining the nests of these communes may in some species be roofed over with earthen plaster. This is occasionally found in the case of the *pratensis* variety of the common wood ant (*Formica rufa*). A related species, *F. integra* of North America, more frequently builds such covered ways.

Most of the commune-forming *Formicinae* are tree-living species. They include such ants as *Oecophylla* from Australia, India, and South Africa, and *Polyrhachis*, another Indo-Australian genus. Both these species build rounded nests actually in the trees. *Oecophylla* is unique in that it builds its nests of leaves which it sews together with the aid of silk produced from the salivary glands of its grubs. It literally uses its grubs as shuttles, weaving them to and fro between the leaves which it has pulled together. *Polyrhachis*, most spiny of all ants and fantastically oriental in appearance, builds nests of cotton on convenient boughs. Like the wood ants, they feed on both insect flesh and the sweet secretions of coccids and other insects yielding honeydew, building earthen or cotton sheds over them to protect them from outside interference – a habit adopted by many other Formicines, though rarely adopted by the *Formicas* themselves.

The Myrmicine *Crematogaster* is another great builder of communes, as is the Dolichoderine *Liometopum*. Both these species are often found nesting in trees as well as on the ground. The Dolichoderine *Iridomyrmex*, including the Cosmopolitan Argentine ant (*I. humilis*), and the Myrmicine *Pogonomyrmex*, are other ground-living commune formers.

All these ants are dominant and highly successful; all are omnivorous, the mighty ones of the ant world. But there are other rival kinds of social ants that by their commoner occurrence are almost equally successful, for large territories are needed to support the vast chains of settlements of the commune ants – territories of equal foraging value. Other social ants form huge colonies containing 100,000 and more individuals. Such are *Camponotus*, rarely a commune-former, *Acanthomyops*, *Prenolepis*, *Plagiolepis* and *Cataglyphis*, among the Formicines; *Dolichoderus* of the Dolichoderines; and *Pheidole*, *Pheidologeton*, *Monomorium*, *Solenopsis* and the *Attini* amongst the Myrmicines. Some like *Pheidole* and *Pheidologeton* are harvesters, living mainly on the sweet sugar from the seeds they garner (see p. 83), but all the same the Myrmicine *Attini*, mushroom-eating leaf cutters of the South American tropics, milk coccids, aphids, and similar plant sap feeders, protecting their herds and choosing their pasture. All but the *Attini* eat flesh food also and all control the territories over which they forage. During the summer months they establish temporary nests along their trails, but these are never queened and are but resting-places for the night, permitting a greater foraging distance from the nest than would otherwise be possible. These can be clearly seen in the European *Acanthomyops* in, for example, both *A. niger* and *A. fuliginosus*, or in the small *Pheidole anastasii* of the Eastern tropics, now the dominant ant of the European hothouses.

But in all these ants, in whatever climates, the work is the same, the governing factors are universal to those already described. Only where the soldier ant is found is there any variation, and that is but slight. These soldiers are a recent development in the ant world, appearing since the Baltic and Sicilian ambers – within the last thirty million years. It is the story of their form and function which leads our discussion onward in Chapter 4.

CHAPTER 4

Strange Societies of Ants

*

SOME of the Social Ants have special large-headed soldier forms, odd ungainly creatures which function as milkers; in breaking the hard outer husks of the grain; as special reserve defenders for the colony who only become active when the colony is excited by attack or other danger; or as janitors, blocking the circular doorways of the nests with their special rounded heads. Other kinds of social ants have special worker individuals who spend whole lives acting as living store-houses for the colony's food. The habits of the Harvesting ants, the Leaf-cutting ants, and the primitive Doryline nomadic Army ants are all remarkable, but strangest of all, perhaps, are the stories of the mixed societies of ants – the slave-makers and their slaves, the thieves and robbers and their victims, the guest ants and their hosts, the odd friendships of the track-sharing ants, and the parasites both temporary and permanent.

Many species of the Social ants have large, small, and intermediate-sized workers. There is no special distinction in either their form or their function and the variation in size is often graded throughout the workers of the colony, with typical and distinct worker-major and worker-minor forms. This is the case in the European and North American *Formicas* and *Acanthomyops*, in the cosmopolitan *Solenopsis* and *Monomorium* and in many of the sub-tropical and tropical *Camponotus*. In nearly every species of ants there is some variation in worker size, but in these large societies that variation has become more and more marked and the largest worker in a colony may well be twice the length of the smallest. In some *Camponotus*, *Azteca*, *Messor* and *Pheidole*, and a few other Formicine, Dolichoderine, and Myrmicine ants, the middle members of the series are lacking and only the distinct worker-major and worker-minor forms are

found. Yet even in these cases experimental work and prolonged observation has failed to show any difference between the function of the two worker types.

In the Harvesting Ants of the genus *Pheidole* and in the
sub-genus *Colobopsis* of *Camponotus* the difference between the
large workers and the small workers is very great, both
anatomically and in their behaviour. In these cases the
worker-major is called a soldier. A similar special soldier
form of worker is found in the Doryline Army ants and in the
primitive Myrmicine genera *Acanthomyrmex* and *Cryptocerus*.

It has frequently been said that in the ants form determines function, and the soldier ants with their special
function have been instanced as being especially important
in this respect. Form, as represented by the major differences between the male, the queen, and the worker, does
indeed determine the basic functions of the individual, but
it is within the worker caste that the greatest flowering
and diversity of behaviour is found. Within the worker
caste, anatomical form determines nothing of the difference
in function in the most highly-developed communities of
the social ants. Only in the case of the few species of ants
which have soldiers – at most three to four hundred species
– can this in any sense be said to be the case.

The Harvesting Ants all belong to the sub-family *Myrmicinae*. In Southern Europe *Messor*, some species of *Pheidole*,
Oxyopomyrmex, and *Goniomma*, all belonging to the *Pheidolini*,
are harvesters. In America, *Veromessor* and *Pogonomyrmex*
of the *Pheidolini* and *Myrmicini* are harvesters, while *Messor*,
which ranges from the Mediterranean to the Cape of Good
Hope in the South and Eastern China in the East, is joined
in Asia by both other species of *Pheidole* and by the genus
Pheidologeton. These Harvesters are only found in regions
south of the 45-degree line of latitude in the northern hemi-
sphere, and only in the grain-producing regions of the
tropics. Typically, they are sub-tropical. Their colonies are
often large, consisting of from ten to sixty thousand individuals, and their nests, which are built in the earth, frequently have a small crater surrounding their entrances.

Within the nest there are special chambers in which the grain is stored. The grain is collected from the growing plant and loose grains on the ground are also gathered in. In Asia, millet grains are collected; in Europe those of wheat. The amount of grain collected by a single nest may often exceed several large cupfuls. The nests are carefully drained, and if by accident, as, for example, through excessive downpours, the grain does become too damp within the subterranean granaries, it is brought up on the first sunny day and, carefully guarded, spread over the ground around the nest to dry. The job of splitting the outer husk is often difficult and is usually done by the larger workers, or, if present, by the soldiers, since their jaws are large enough to grip the slippery casing, and their jaw muscles are larger and stronger. The placing of the seeds in the sun also helps the change of the inedible starch inside the seed into edible and attractive sugar (see p. 7).

The *Pheidole* soldiers are for most of the time lazy, slow-moving creatures. They differ from the workers solely in their larger overall size and in the size and shape of their heads. These heads are rectangular in shape and often as long as the rest of the body put together and wider than the gaster. The eyes and antennae are relatively small, and at the front end above the mouth there is an appropriately-sized pair of jaws. Needless to say, mobility is not the main characteristic of these monstrous-headed creatures. They wander listlessly up and down the trails in amongst the hurrying workers, but do no work. Indeed, they only become active when the workers themselves become more than normally excited. Then all of a sudden, as if some threshold had been reached which switched them on, they rush out of the nest and run around snapping their immense jaws at any foreign creature that comes within range. Except for their occasional aid in the cutting of seed casings, this is the sole contribution to the colony economy.

In the Formicine *Colobopsis*, an omnivorous, widely-distributed ant which lives in smallish colonies of a thousand or two thousand individuals, the soldier is differently formed and has an even more closely-defined function. *Colobopsis* are found throughout much of the world : in South America, in Texas, in the East Indies, and even, represented by *C. truncatus*, in the warmer regions of Europe. Always they live in twigs, or within the branches of trees, gall nuts, or bamboo. Each nest has but a single entrance, which is cut out of the outer bark and is small and of a circular shape. These entrances are very difficult to find unless the movements of the foraging workers are followed with the greatest care, for the only sign of them will be the sudden appearance of a dark round hole just near a scurrying worker, through which it will dive, only for the hole to disappear immediately. The opening and closing of the hole is due to the retreat of the janitor to let the scurrying workers in and her sudden re-appearance. For it is her head which, well armoured, specially rounded, and matching in colour the surface of the twig or branch, has blocked the hole and forms the door. Although we know little of their habits, the function of the concave-headed soldiers of *Cryptocerus* and the rare *Acanthomyrmex* are almost certainly similar.

The other large group of ants in which soldiers are found is that of the Army Ants – the *Dorylinae*, the dreaded 'Isanafu' of Africa, India, and South America. Confined to the tropics, it is in Africa and Central and South America that they are most important and most feared. Represented in Africa by *Dorylus* and in South America by *Eciton*, both of which genera have several sub-genera and a few less noteworthy smaller cousin genera, the raids of the legionaries have long been known. Yet it is only in the last few years that we have begun to understand their habits. It was commonly thought that they marched because they had consumed all the food in their nest area and that this explained their forays, in which the whole colony takes part, the queen marching with the workers or being half dragged, half carried by them along with the grubs and cocoons. They were in search of a new and more well-stocked territory and naturally lived on the land as they went. Living on the land is scarcely an adequate description of their behaviour while on the march, for large animals as well as other insects fear their approach and flee before it. If a horse be left tethered and cannot break loose it will be eaten and left a skeleton where it stands. A troop of birds wheels above to eat the tit-bits which their coming starts from cover, and the foetid smell of carrion swathes their ranks. Never deviating, they go onwards, cutting a swathe feet thick through the ranks of living creatures on their trail. Sickle-jawed soldiers outside, workers inside, the column marches steadily with outriders all around searching every nook and cranny for the half-gallon of booty needed each day to feed the eighty thousand adults and their thirty thousand worm-like, squirming brood. If a house is in their way they enter it, clean it out, and leave it free of vermin – a service that earns them tolerance and even welcome from the native villages *en route*. Only a few insects can survive their passage and most of these are ants like Dolichoderines, whose repugnatorial glands drive even them away, the social Formicines, whose large colonies they dare not tackle, and some odd Myricines and Ponerines too heavily armoured to be bitten or too fierce.

The legend of their nomadism is only half the truth. They never settle down. Their raids are not just a passage to a new site where food is more abundant, but a constant cycle, immutable and quite separate from all factors save the appearance, growth, and hatching of the brood. Every thirty or forty days, depending on the species, the monstrous queen lays a vast batch of eggs. The whole egg mass consisting of some twenty-five to thirty-five thousand eggs is produced within two days. The colony has stopped marching two or three days before this event and remains resting, foraging locally and tending the new-born larvae which quickly hatch from the eggs, until towards the middle or end of the third week the vast mass of cocoons from the previous generation begin to hatch out. This incursion of new adults, both worker and soldier, into their ranks sets off the marching stage of the cycle. Within two or three days they are off: the whole colony is on the move. For ten to eighteen days they march and hunt, forming only temporary burrows each night (or in the dry season each day). Then as the queen fattens again with eggs they stop and the cycle re-commences. Year in, year out, the discipline goes on – march, rest, march, rest, never more than three and a half weeks in any single spot. The hatching-out of the males merely takes the place of a single worker generation. Having started off the march by their appearance, they disappear two or three days later in ones and twos, then scores and hundreds each following night or day, as the march goes on, or as bivouac is broken. Their marching has helped them perhaps to learn to pick up trails of other raiding colonies when they land, for being the winged sex (with queen unwinged), they must fly off and seek their mates in other colonies on the trail.

Before turning to the mixed colonies of ants something must be said of the leaf-cutting ants and their mushroom-forming, and of the honey-pot ants and their living pots.

The fungus-growing ants all belong to the *Attini*, a tribe of social *Myrmicinae*, which is confined to South America. Their colonies usually consist of about 60,000 individuals and their spiky workers vary greatly in size, though not in what they do. They have no soldier caste. There are several queens in most *Attini* colonies, and each one of them brings with her as dowry to the home she founds a minute mycelium of mushroom spores, which she carries in the sac below her mouth, the infra-buccal chamber. It is this mycelium carried by the founder queen which forms the basis of the original mushroom garden of the colony. The provisions of the later queens are not vital unless the garden prove unhealthy. But each queen must carry spores, since most have to try and found new colonies even though they perish in the attempt, and without this food their offspring could not live. During the early days of an *Attini* colony the queen tends the mushroom growth herself, setting it out on a bed of chewed leaf mould and manuring it with her own excreta. Later on, when her brood are well grown, they set out each day in vast numbers to strip the nearby trees. On their return to the nest each one carries parasol-like over her back a rounded section of the scissored leaf. All these leaves are used to make mulch for the fungus beds, a process which involves hours of lengthy chewing when the leaf-bearers have reached the nest. The fungus is a species of *Rhozites* (*R. ganglyophora*) and would, if allowed to grow, develop into a large mushroom six or seven inches tall. The ants never let it reach a size of more than a few millimetres in length, cutting it off and constantly re-planting the mycelium in a further part of the chamber or in new chambers. The propagation within the nest is thus purely vegetative, the reproductive stages never being attained. The balance between food supply and population is delicate. Too few workers will be unable to keep a large mushroom garden in check and will have to flee before its rapid growth and spreading. Too many workers, on the other hand, would starve.

The honey-pot ants were first found in the Valley of the Gods in Colorado. Since then ants with similar habits, though not developed to the same degree, have been found in other parts of the world. The original honey-pot ants belong to the sub-genus of *Camponotus*, *Myrmecocystus*, and are named *hortus-deorum* after the place in which they were found. The majority of the workers are perfectly normal in appearance – black, largish, omnivorous foragers, returning home with full but not abnormally swollen crops. When swollen, the crops of most social ants become so distended as to push apart the plates of their gasters, exposing the elastic joints which hold them together. This gives their gasters a stripy appearance, light yellowish stripes alternating with the darker armoured segments. In *M. hortus-deorum* this distension is taken to extreme lengths in a few score individuals. They hang immobile from the roof of one of the lower chambers of the nest, unable to leave the ceiling because of their fantastically swollen gasters, one-third of an inch in diameter. If they fall their feet wave helplessly in the air, kept from the ground by the bulk of their spherical abdomens. If they chance to split their overloaded crops in falling, as sometimes happens, then the other workers rush to enjoy the food released by the catastrophe, caring nothing for the fate of the individual to whom it has occurred. These honey-pots have no special anatomical differences from those they serve. They are perfectly normal workers, who, though starting from earliest adult days to strain their crops to inordinate lengths, soon have a special facility in this direction. Once started, there is no return – the constant feeding of the other workers sees to that. More and more food is housed inside them by hundreds of daily regurgitations. The rest of the organs of their gaster are squeezed aside until eventually they occupy but a fraction of the space and the social stomach and handy pannier for the carrying of food becomes the communal storage bin, holding the colony's food reserves and saving it from starvation when food is scarce. *Myrmecocystus melliger* of Mexico, another honey-pot ant, often sought by natives as a luxury for their wedding banquets, the Dolichoderine *Leptomyrmex* and the Formicine *Melophorus* of Australia, and other species in which this habit is less well developed, all live in dry, arid country where water is scarce and rains are far between. The habit enables them to survive long droughts during which they would otherwise suffer both lack of food and desiccation.

Although this behaviour is certainly instinctive, it is not so fixed that individual choice is pre-determined. All the workers of the colony could become honey-pots; few do. The choice is made by circumstance. More honey-pots are needed and a young ant is nearby (for the honey-pots naturally hang near the brood as being precious possessions of the colony), perhaps even feeding for a honey-pot, when the need for a new one becomes apparent. All are full, or nearly so, and closing their mouths against a further store. The young ant gladly accepts the proffered drop, then more, and more, for other workers soon besiege her. Soon she is fattening and climbs for comfort slowly upwards while she can still use her legs. She has joined the ranks and her fate is sealed.

It is indeed in the realm of facultative, or if not optional behaviour (for the young *Myrmecocystus* had little option except to behave abnormally and refuse the proffered drops), at least not instinctively fixed and pre-determined behaviour, that the most fascinating behaviour of the ant is found : behaviour which really raises a pucker on the brow when an answer is sought to the problem of how near to insight, or to reason, do the ants approach. Some part of this problem becomes apparent as the story of the mixed colonies of different species of ants unfolds.

It is natural that in such dominant and world-wide social creatures as the ants, who struggle and compete more with one another than with creatures of a different kind, some strange liaisons should be formed. Where two species, perhaps of widely different origins, have the same demands, the same needs of food and home and climate, they do not always compete, fighting and destroying each other for possession of the things they both need. Instead they form a pact, either temporary or more permanent, often going to the utmost limits of share and share alike. This is but one aspect of a story that must start a little further back.

The many inter-relationships between the different species of ants can be divided conveniently into two main groups – those which are obligatory, so fixed in habit that they cannot be altered; and those which are facultative or even casual, which are, however, frequent in occurrence, in no way fixed pre-requisites of the ants' survival. The plan opposite gives an outline of the further groups which follow from this major one and provides a convenient key to the story which is about to be told.

All the subsequent relationships between one species of ants and another come from simple fundamental events of only two types. In the first place ants, as has been seen, have much contact with other species of ants during their lives. They meet other ants, they may even eat other ants – a more frequent event than is sometimes realized – and the social ants compete with other species of ants for the dominion, maintenance, and extension of their foraging and nesting territory.

Table showing the chief types of relationships found between different species of Ants*

A. CASUAL AND FACULTATIVE RELATIONSHIPS

1. *Casual competitive relationships*
   (a) Preying
   (b) Interterritorial competition

2. *Facultative competitive relationships*
   (a) Facultative slave-making

3. *Facultative non-competitive relationships*
   (a) Originally casual colonial associations (*plesiobiosis*)
   (b) Track-sharing (*parabiosis*)
   (c) The relations of normally non-competitive species occurring in the same habitat

B. OBLIGATORY RELATIONSHIPS

1. *Obligatory tolerant or co-operative relationships*
   (a) Guestship (*xenobiosis*)
   (b) Soldiership (*phylacobiosis*)

2. *Obligatory competitive relationships*
   (a) *Intra-nidal*
      1. Obligatory slave-making (*dulosis*)
      2. Temporary social parasitism
      3. Permanent social parasitism (*colacobiosis*)

   (b) *Extra-nidal*
      1. Thieving (*lestobiosis*)
      2. Robbing (*cleptobiosis*)

* *The Latin names in brackets have been included to facilitate reference to scientific papers in which they occur. Their use should be avoided. It is quite unnecessary.*

In the second place the simple marriage flight of the queens and males leaves newly fertilized queens wandering and seeking shelter wherein they can safely fix their abode and set about the task of founding a new colony. This simple pattern has often become varied, and that variation results in some of the behaviour patterns, both facultative and obligatory, which form the subject of a part of this discussion. But it was the primitive simple marriage flight followed by the solitary unaided attempt to found a new colony which gave rise to all other forms of colony foundation.

The meeting of the other species of ants led to preying on them and preying on other species of ants led to the stealing of attractive booty – booty made precious both by habitual association of its value within their own nests, by the attempts to carry it away from the attackers, and by its greater edibility. This booty is, of course, the brood, both grubs and larvae. Both were stolen in the first place as food. This still happens when one species of ant makes war on another ant. The victors eat the grubs and pupae on their return to their nest. Sometimes, however, one or even more of the pupae may hatch out, even perhaps helped by the cutting of the outer skin or casing by the would-be feaster. Once this happens, the meal is at an end, for the ant just hatching rouses instincts of helping in the capturer. When at last it is out and freely moving it is no longer an enemy. It has no hostile nest odour. It is indistinguishable to the victors from one of their own young. It in turn has known no other colleagues, and accepts the victors as its own kin. Soon the victors make it even more one of the family by licking it and feeding it. Thus sometimes odd individuals of a different species may come to live as fellow ants in colonies to which they were born as strangers. This event is very rare, but it does happen. The slave-making ants *Formica sanguinea* and (more rarely) *Polyergus rufescens* frequently steal the pupae of ants not belonging to slave species as food – for example those of *Acanthomyops fuliginosus*, the Jet Ant, or *Myrmica*, and occasionally bring them to maturity, while such odd individuals of different species are sometimes found in the

nests of other species fully accepted as colleagues and fellow
members of the community. There is no doubt it was thus
that the acquisition of slaves began.

In the same way the strangest neighbours may come to
share the same stone as a roof to their nest as the result of a
casual event following the marriage flight. When the queen
reaches the ground after the nuptial flight, shelter and
security are her dominant desires. She must find a hole in
the ground, in or under a log, or under a stone where she
can hide and start her task of colony foundation. Not infrequently several queens will crawl under the same stone or
into the same hole. When this happens the situation is amicably accepted. Too many queens will not indeed remain in
the same spot, but two or three or even four may often be
found together in a single earthen cell under the same stone.
The relationship is usually quite satisfactorily maintained
until the first workers appear and the colony is established.
A small colony of normally prolific species will not support
more than one or two queens, and there is a division of
loyalties between them which ends in the unwanted queen
or queens being driven from the nest. When the colony is
mature and has a more normal population, extra queens
are sought, but in these early days it is rare for more than
two, or at most three, to be allowed to stay in the colony.
Sometimes the queens scurrying under a single stone are
not aware that others have already established themselves
in its shelter. The stone is large and they crawl under it at a
different point. Finding no objectionable or dangerous occu-
pant, they rest awhile, then start to excavate a small chamber, piling up the dug earth around the sides. The long
period of waiting and of feeding the young larvae from the
food absorbed into her stomach from her own body then
begins. Eventually the new colony is successfully established,
and the workers begin to excavate new chambers to house
the expanding nest. Deeper chambers are built connected to
the upper ones by passages, and passages and chambers expand outwards on either side. Eventually the discovery is
made. Other ants are also living under the same stone. They

smell different. Not very different, but definitely not quite the same. In such cases the two colonies nearly always amalgamate – the difference between their nest odours is not great. They are of the same species and have the same basic odours and the materials of which their nests are made could scarcely be more similar. In any case, a period of close familiarity in which the two colonies are only separated by a thin wall usually acclimatizes them to the differences which exist, to such a point that they are finally accepted and the barrier between the two colonies is removed.

Clearly such an event may have other consequences than those just retailed. If two queens of the same species can unawares found colonies of the same species under a single stone, so can two queens of different species. Providing that the brood of one of the queens (or one set of queens) does not develop so quickly that her adult offspring appear long before those of her hidden neighbour and so do not discover her before her own brood are well established, two colonies will again be established, but this time of different species. The same expansion of the nest takes place. The same discovery is made, followed by hurried withdrawal and speedy building operations to wall the strangers off. As the nest expands, the contacts become more frequent and eventually a series of walled barriers at each level of the nests is all that separates the two colonies. Once again a certain familiarity with the neighbours' nest odour results and the position is tacitly accepted. This time there is no breaking of the barriers. The barriers remain intact; the colonies do not amalgamate, but they do accept one another's proximity and rarely quarrel when they meet outside on their respective foraging expeditions. This is the most primitive form of peaceful association between nests of two different species of ants. It differs from that of the slave-makers and their slaves in that the queens, brood, and workers are all involved. In this simple casual relationship the peace can often be easily disrupted. All that is needed is the removal of the barriers, or if the nest be under a stone the removal of this roof, which has the same effect. Then there is fighting which rarely ceases until one or other side has been massacred or has fled. The disturbance of the nests excites the ants and the removal of the barrier directs the pugnacity evoked by the interference against one another. Without such human interference such colonies will live in neighbourly peace and mutual tolerance for many years. They are most frequent under stones because of the attraction of stones as a nesting-place for many species of ants like our European *Myrmicas* and the yellow species of *Acanthomyops* (e.g. *A. flavus* and *mixtus*). The stones make convenient hiding-places for the newly wed queen and form a convenient protective roofing for the nest: a roof, moreover, that will absorb and retain the heat of the sun, providing well-protected warm chambers beneath in which the brood can be gathered in perfect safety. They provide in fact most of the benefits of a solarium with much superior protection. On the other hand, stones are usually far too small for the needs of the really populous ant communities. Such side-by-side communities are found in earthen banks, in trees, and, indeed, in all the many types of nesting-places where ants are found. In most of these there are less well-defined limits to their spread than those formed by the confines of a stone. The ants are freer to draw more apart one from another and the relationship is usually less apparent if not less close.

These simple casual associations between *Myrmica* and *Acanthomyops*, *Myrmica* and *Formica fusca*, or *Acanthomyops niger* and *Ac. Flavus* or *Ac. mixtus* are, however, undoubtedly the source from which other more complex associations are derived.

One such more complex relationship is that of track-sharing. This reaches its highest form in cases like one found by the Swiss ant student Auguste Forel in Colombia. Here a Myrmicine ant, *Crematogaster limata*, and a Dolichoderine ant, *Dolichoderus* (*Monacis*) *debilis*, were not only living in what was to all intents and purposes a single nest, though keeping their nest chambers and broods and queens apart, but were forming joint foraging trails. Workers of both species set out along the same routes, only separating when they reached the bushes which they had set out to visit. Then the much larger *Monacis* (*Monacis* is a sub-genus of *Dolichoderus*) set out for the nectaries of the flowers and the *Crematogaster* went off to milk their aphid herds. Even Forel's breaking open of the joint nest, which was in an abandoned Termite nest, did not cause a battle. Each species withdrew further into its own chambers. Both these species and even these particular local races (which Forel named *parabiotica* in both cases to commemorate this event) are usually found living quite separately with no neighbour species. A somewhat similar state of affairs to this exists in the case of the Tree Ants of Southern North America, Central America, and the West Indies, where six or eight species of ants may be found living in the same *Tillandsia* tree. The ants do not form shared trails or mix together, but they do not fight when they meet, as they are constantly doing, each time they set out foraging. Species of such diverse origin as the Pseudomyrmine *Pseudomyrma*, the Myrmicine *Monomorium*, *Xenomyrmex*, *Crematogaster*, *Leptothorax*, and *Cryptocerus*, and the Dolichoderine *Tapinoma* and Formicine *Camponotus*, are frequently found nesting in the same tree. Another variety of the same *Monacis* species *debilis*, called *rufescens*, has even been found living in this side-by-side track-sharing relationship with a Brazilian Ponerine ant, *Odontomachus affinis*, one of the 'Tak' ants : while a *Camponotus* of the sub-genus *Myrmobrachis* and a *Pseudomyrma* were found by another ant student, Morton Wheeler, in Central America, living in different thorns of an *Acacia*, but going out together to forage.

These relationships can sometimes turn into less amicable ones where one species, while peacefully tolerated by the other, steals food and even grubs and pupae from it. This is most frequent in the case of the simpler casual relationships like those between the European Yellow Hill Ant *Acanthomyops flavus* and the Red Ant *Myrmica rubra*, where the latter, while living in part of the Yellow Ants' hill, steals food both from individuals and from the nest itself.

All the relationships so far described have been faculta-

1. Honeypot ants (*Myrmecocystus hortideorum*) from the Garden of the Gods, Colorado (*from a drawing by Murayama after H.C. McCook*).

2. South American Army Ant, *Eciton hamatum*, forming nest beneath log.

3. Wood Ant (*Formica rufa L.*) *at the alert.*

4. Two wood ants tap feelers.

5 and 6. Wood ants fighting.

7. A spiny *Polyrhachis* from India.

8. Two Burmese primitive formicine *Opisthopis* (see p. 52) at play.

9. Tree ant, *Oecophylla smaragdina*, from India using its grubs as shuttles in weaving their nest.

10

10 and 11. Wood ant worker (*Formica rufa L.*) holds a Yellow Lawn Ant worker (*Acanthomyops mixtus*) in its jaws while squirting it with formic acid.

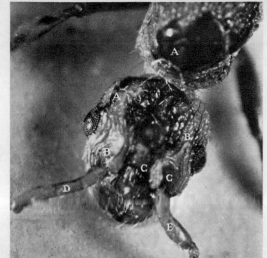

A. Dark strips of male tissue.

B. Light female tissue.

C. Dark patches of male tissue.

D. Long female antenna.

E. Short male antenna.

12.

12. A jig-saw ant from Ireland's Eye: gynandromorph of *Myrmica rubra sabuleti*.

13. Close-up of wood ant feeding on sugar.

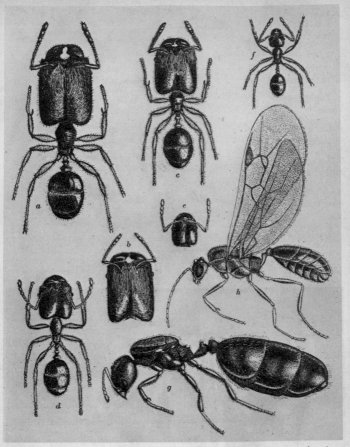

14. *Pheidole instabilis*, a harvesting ant, showing the extreme development of the worker and soldier castes (*after Wheeler*).

a. Soldier ; *b – e.* intermediate workers ; *f.* typical worker (micrergate) ; *g.* deälated female ; *h.* male.

tive. They are not habits indulged in by all the members of the species, each one of which can live quite happily without the other species and in most cases is more usually found living alone. Before considering the obligatory liaisons in which all members of the species involved must necessarily indulge, mention must be made of the facultative guest ant, *Leptothorax acervorum*, and the slave raids of the slave-maker *Formica sanguinea* must be described. The habits of *Leptothorax acervorum* will be more fully described along with those of its cousins, *L. emersoni* and *L. glacialis*, and its fellow Myrmicine *Formicoxenus nitidulus*, which, unlike *L. acervorum*, are only found living as guests in the nests of other species of ants and never living on their own. Although *L. acervorum* is most frequently found in the nests of one of the *Formica* wood ants, it is also much more commonly found living alone than is usually believed. Thousands of colonies of this small Myrmicine can be found hundreds of miles away from the nearest Wood Ant nest on Howth Head, near Dublin, and there are many such colonies in Wytham Wood, near Oxford, and along the cliffs beyond Swanage in Dorsetshire.

The Blood Red slave-making ant *Formica sanguinea*, on the other hand, is rarely found nesting alone without its slaves in Britain. Only two or three records of flourishing *sanguinea* colonies in which no slaves were present have been recorded from this country. In both Europe, Northern Asia and Japan, and North America, where it is much more abundant, there are records of numerous colonies of these ants in which, even when they have been visited over a period of several years, slaves have never been present. There is no doubt that the Blood Red slave-maker can live quite happily and successfully without its slaves. It can feed itself, fight, forage, and perform all the duties of the community. Frequently, both in the presence of slaves and in their absence, it forms large communes consisting of a score or more nests. One such commune even had more than forty nests. Few *sanguinea* live in solitary nests and few of their communes have less than five nests, or settlements. These settlements are not very populous, containing only a thousand or so individuals, the whole commune comprising between 5,000 and 10,000 individuals. Many communes may contain far less than this number of *sanguinea* workers, but when this occurs the deficiency is usually to some extent, if not completely, made up by the presence of numerous slaves. The number of slaves is related to the needs of the colony and varies from year to year. A populous commune containing 5,000 or more *sanguinea* will contain only 50 to 100 slaves. But a commune having a population of only 2,000 *sanguinea* will usually contain between 400 and 500 slaves. An even smaller *sanguinea* colony having, say, 800 *sanguinea* will have approximately the same number of slave ants. The greater the need of the slave-makers for extra numbers, the greater the number of slaves. Populous colonies make few if any slave raids, while smaller colonies will often make frequent slave-making expeditions. As the slave ants live more than a year – usually for at least two or three years – the number of slaves in a colony will not lessen by much during the first two years succeeding a low *sanguinea* population and consequent heavy slave-raiding. In the third year the number of slaves in the nest will drop heavily unless their presence during the previous years has failed to restore the commune's economy and consequently the fertility and population of the *sanguineas*. If the *sanguinea* population is still low, the third year will again be a heavy raiding year and the cycle will continue until the *sanguinea* population improves. Although most moderately-sized *sanguinea* colonies make some raids each year, the number of slaves in their nests practically never exceeds 1,000 and rarely attains the four-figure mark. Only in the weakest of *sanguinea* colonies is the slave-maker outnumbered, an event which is for some reason quite usual in North America, where the *sanguinea* colonies are nearly always smaller, though rare in other parts of the world.

The slaves of *F. sanguinea* always belong to closely-related species. Their most usual slave is the Large Black Ant *Formica fusca*, but nests of *F. rufa* and its sub-species *pratensis*,

F. exsecta, F. pallide-fulva, F. cinerea, and *fusca's* close cousin
F. rufibarbis may be raided. Of these species *pallide-fulva* and
cinerea are confined to America. One of the American sub-
species of *sanguinea, F. aserva,* whose Latin name *aserva* means
'slaveless', is not known to make slaves, nor is the closely-
related *Formica munda.* Another close cousin, *F. pergandei,* is,
however, a slave-maker and raids the same three major
groups of *Formica* species, *rufa, fusca,* and *pallide-fulva.*

The species enslaved depends on the availability of the
various slave-species. A single commune may contain several
species of slaves – a mixture which tells the history of their
raids. *Rufa, fusca* and the Ruddy Black Ant *rufibarbis,* all
mingle together with the *sanguinea.*

The slave raids take place in high summer, during the
months of July and August. For several days before the raid
itself takes place, individual *sanguinea,* travelling singly or in
groups of two or three, scout out the nest which is to be
attacked. Then, as soon as the sun is warm on the chosen
day, small masses of *sanguinea* begin to collect around their
nests. Towards noon, three or four parties of between 50
and 200 individuals each, led by a scout, set off from the
commune advancing at a quick pace in the general direction
of the enemy. The direct route to the fortress of the slaves
is avoided by most if not all of the parties which approach
the nest simultaneously from several directions. On drawing
near to the hostile nest, a halt is called. Then, while the other
parties remain outside spread round the nest and establish-
ing a blockade, one group makes a fierce assault. If possible
this is done from one side, not in the quarter of the main
entrance, especially if the enemy nest be a settlement of one
of the large Wood Ant communes. The assaulting party rush
impetuously within the enemy nest, dragging the defenders
with them, who try to stop them. Once inside they head
straight for the chambers containing the brood, each *sanguinea* endeavouring to seize a cocoon. Finding their brood
at the mercy of the intruders, the defenders seek to save their
grubs and pupae by flight, and rush from the nest bearing
them away in their jaws. The result is only more disaster,

for the waiting blockaders seize them as they sally forth and relieve them of their charges. As each *sanguinea* worker obtains a pupa it sets off on the return journey to its own home, often twenty or thirty yards away. The whole exercise is a remarkable exhibition of military tactics and the result, despite the empty-handed return of many of the warriors, like those of the first rush and most of the rearguard, is the increase of the numbers of the colony by two, if not three, hundred or more individuals. The *sanguinea* losses rarely exceed a score or two, chiefly those engaged in the first assault. In a large raid, simultaneous assaults from two directions may be made, but this is a rare occurrence, the single spearhead attack coupled with an efficient blockade seeming to serve the purpose best.

Polyergus, another Formicine slave-maker which makes its slaves from similar species, is represented in Europe and Asia by *P. rufescens* and in America by *P. lucidus*. These ants have to make slaves : they cannot even feed themselves and die without the aid of slaves to care for them. They also send out scouts, but instead of using the canny tactics of the *sanguinea*, they set out in vast armies of serried ranks directly *en masse* to the hostile nest. Their route is the straightest that is possible and the attack is made by the whole body of the army. Their sickle jaws are so ill-adapted for handling food in small enough quantities that they are literally unable to eat without being handed food direct to their mouths. But they are most effective weapons of warfare, their pointed ends piercing the heads of their adversaries in a manner that a more normal blunt-ended toothed mandible cannot. Their raids are usually of equal success, though the casualties may be greater. Again they rely in the main on the shock and drive of the assault to win the day against vastly superior numbers. But the fate of *Polyergus* is not so happy a one as that of *sanguinea*. They need numerous slaves – several thousands instead of several hundreds – and are completely dependent. Unlike *sanguinea*, they are unable to found new colonies without their aid and the newly-fertilized queen must needs make a solitary single-handed raid to steal cocoons for slaves to tend her and rear her brood. They are not indeed so far removed from the sad degeneration of *Harpagoxenus* and *Strongylognathus*, the Myrmicine slave-raiders which have in some cases developed into little more than parasites.

The raids of *Harpagoxenus* show none of the organization characteristics of *Polyergus*. They collect indeed at the entrance to their nest before the raid, making a fine show of deeds to be done, and surrounded and solicitously tended by their slaves. But what follows is anticlimax indeed. They amble off singly, or at most in twos and threes, towards the hostile nest – in this case that of another Myrmicine, *Leptothorax*. Arrived at the nest, they walk straight in, ignoring any attempt to stop them. The single *Harpagoxenus* just persists in going quietly on towards the brood. Having reached it, it seizes a pupa and as sedately yet determinedly emerges and plods off home. It seems scarcely possible that this weakened creature can fight, yet its sickle-shaped jaws (typical of all obligatory slave-makers) are still capable of piercing an enemy head.

Strongylognathus diveri, however, is even more decayed. It lives in a few colonies of the Turf ant *Tetramorium caespitum* at Studland, on the borders of the New Forest, a permanent parasite, no longer capable of raiding and barely surviving. It is the end result of what can clearly be seen to be happening in the case of its Swiss relative *S. testaceus*, large numbers of whose queens and males are to be found in the *T. caespitum* nests, but few workers. The worker caste is disappearing. Yet its related species, *S. alpina*, are still active raiders and even the weaker *S. huberi* can certainly still achieve successful raids against the the warlike *T. caespitum*.

The end result of such obligatory slave-making is more clearly seen in the European *Anergates* and the Central African *Anergatides*. Both related to *Harpagoxenus*, they represent the depths of ant degeneracy. Neither *Anergates atratulus* nor *Anergatides kohli* have any workers. In both the male is a degenerate, wingless creature, which is more like a legged and crawling pupa than an adult ant. This is especially the case in *Anergates*. Both ants are rare. *Anergates* is found in the nests of *Tetramorium caespitum* and *Anergatides* in those of *Pheidole megacephala*. In the nests where they are found the host queen is lacking. In *Anergates*, whose habits are better known, the fertile queen reaches an emormous size when she is swollen with eggs, but with her immensely swollen gaster is quite incapable of movement. All her eggs turn into either sickly crumpled, yellowish males or into winged queens, many of which will be seen running to and fro in the nest amongst the *Tetramorium* workers. The mating of the virgin queens and males takes place within the nest or just outside it. All these matings take place on the same day and afterwards the queens fly off, seek out new *Tetramorium* nests and entering them are willingly accepted by the workers. Once established in the nest the *Anergates* queen usurps the place of the *Tetramorium* queens, who are killed by their own offspring. The males of these two parasitic genera are remarkable not only for their immature form, but also because, like the larvae and pupae, they are especially attractive to the *Tetramorium* and *Pheidole* workers, who constantly lick them and seem to gain great pleasure from this action.

The killing of the queens of the host species is also an important event in the cases of temporary parasitism which form an intermediate stage of the process of colony foundation in many species of *Formica* and *Acanthomyops*. It is a necessary part of the process of adoption because the incoming queen must establish herself as the producer of the grubs and pupae so desired by the workers (see p. 29). The queens of the vast colonies and communes of *Formica* and *Acanthomyops* often develop their fertility slowly. They find it difficult, if not impossible, to found a colony entirely unaided and either, as in *Formica rufa*, take with them some workers from their own colony, or else seek acceptance in other colonies of their own species, or in those of other species. Some species, like *F. rufa*, are not entirely dependent on the help of other species, but others, such as *F. microgyna* of North America and *Acanthomyops fuliginosus* of Europe and northern Asia, are quite unable to found new colonies without passing through a stage of temporary parasitism.

The first need of the newly-fertilized queen is to obtain acceptance in the nest of the other species – usually a related kind, e.g. *Acanthomyops mixtus* or *niger* in the case of *A. fuliginosus*. She does this by first venturing near the nest, but not within it for a period of one or two days, or occasionally longer. Then, entering the nest, she presses towards the chambers of the queens and brood, struggling inwards despite the puzzled tuggings and rather vague attacks of the hostile workers. They are puzzled because of her strangeness, and yet she has a vague familiarity due to her partial infection with their own nest odour during her period of waiting in the vicinity of their nest. It is essential that she reach a fertile queen as soon as possible and she struggles onwards towards that goal. Her life depends upon success. Once her purpose is achieved she mounts the back of the enemy queen and saws off its head, the odour of her victim providing protection for her during the process. Nothing then remains except for her to take the old queen's place, lay her eggs and produce her young. The other queens of the host species are not killed – they are merely not replaced when they die. And so for five, ten, or even more years the colony becomes a mixed one. *A. fuliginosus* and *A. mixtus* live together in amity sharing food and brood. Jet Black Ants and Yellow Lawn Ants mingle on the trails, making a pretty sight of peaceful co-operation which somewhat belies the more sordid history. The appearance of the normally completely troglodytic Yellow Lawn Ants on the outdoor trails of the mixed colony is one of the most extraordinary reversals of normal and supposedly instinctive behaviour in the whole of ant life. As the *mixtus* queens die and the remaining old ones lose their fertility, the *mixtus* workers disappear from the trails. The colony ceases to be mixed and becomes at last a new pure *fuliginosus* one.

This temporary parasitism must not be confused with that of *Anergates* and other degenerate ants. It results rather from the renewed division of the fertility in the higher Formicines plus the vast fertility required from each queen in order to provide the vast numbers of their colonies. Its origins are different – owing more to a slower development of fertility and a smaller size of queen, coupled with a greater degree of psychological, as against physical, development and specialization. The answers to the problem of the Formicines are usually behavioural ones, not such as involve change in form or physique. The greater familiarity with different species is reflected in this bold invasion of another ants' nest, as is also the basic element of the casual proximity of the fertile female to that nest after the marriage flight – an element not so dissimilar from that described earlier in the history of the neighbour colonies (see p. 94).

Not all mixed colonies which are obligatory are also parasitic. More so are the thief ants like *Solenopsis fugax*, which builds its minute passages within the walls of the nests of other larger ants, which it robs, and the Dolichoderine scavenger ants who reside nearby, but not within the nests of other ants, and make darting raids upon the laden homecomers. But the guest ants are neither parasites nor robbers. Typified by *Leptothorax* (several species) and by *Formicoxenus nitidulus*, they live within the nests of other species which are often (though not always) most distantly related. The parasitic species of ants, on the other hand, all live in the nests of close relatives. The communities of these guest ants are intimately bound up with those of their hosts and yet seem to give no special gain to the hosts (except in the case of *L. emersoni* – see p. 22) and yet to take nothing from them. The nests are kept separate and the much smaller guests go out and forage on the Wood Ant trails. They gain protection by their association, and if the Wood Ants move, move with them to the new nest. In the case of *L. acervorum* it is clear that its habit of nesting in decaying stumps of trees and twigs, which former liking is shared by *Formica rufa* and other wood ants (see p. 72), has had much to do with the forming of the, in this case, non-obligatory association. Probably the relationship between *Formicoxenus* and the woodland *Formicas* originally evolved in a similar manner.

One further type of mixed community must be mentioned, and that is a peculiar friendship between ants and Termites. Only two cases are known of this odd behaviour, in which the ants seem to act as soldiers for the Termite colonies they inhabit in return for hospitality and shelter. The first of these associations was described by the Jesuit ant student, Wasmann, in 1901–2, between the Formicine *Camponotus termitarius* and *Eutermes fulviceps*. The second instance was described in a letter to the author from Dr Julian Huxley, who observed it in West Africa in 1945. In this latter case each of half a dozen Termite colonies broken open were found to contain a large Camponotoid ant which immediately rushed out to defend the colony.

It is now time to consider the ants' perception of the world around them, before returning to discuss the successes and failures of their societies in the world at large.

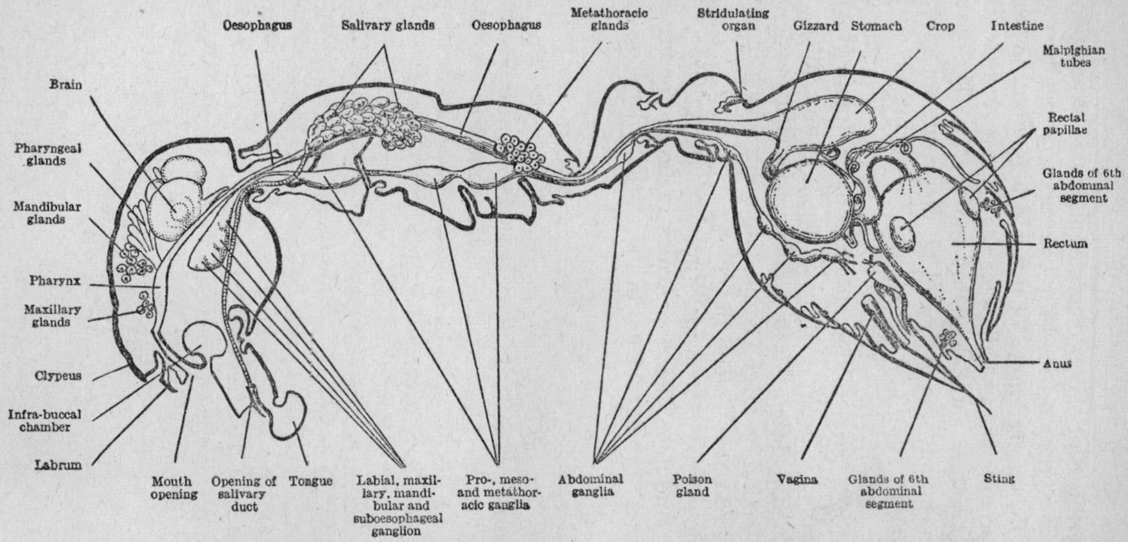
Oesophagus
Salivary glands
Oesophagus
Metathoracic glands
Stridulating organ
Gizzard
Stomach
Crop
Intestine
Malpighian tubes
Rectal papillae
Glands of 6th abdominal segment
Rectum
Anus
Brain
Pharyngeal glands
Mandibular glands
Pharynx
Maxillary glands
Clypeus
Infra-buccal chamber
Labrum
Mouth opening
Opening of salivary duct
Tongue
Labial, maxillary, mandibular and suboesophageal ganglion
Pro-, meso- and metathoracic ganglia
Abdominal ganglia
Poison gland
Vagina
Glands of 6th abdominal segment
Sting

Myrmica rubra (female): internal structure (after Janet)

CHAPTER 5

The Sensory World of the Ants

*

ANTS have most of the senses we human beings have, but usually in somewhat different forms. They can smell through their antennal noses. They can in most cases see, though often poorly, through their faceted compound eyes, and also, somewhat differently, through the two or three simple single-lensed eyes which are often present on the back of their heads. They can taste food, but differently from us, since their antennal noses are quite separate from their mouths, unlike our noses and tongues. The two sets of sensations are consequently more distinct. The ants' sense of touch is well developed, as befits animals in whom the sense of sight is not dominant. They can feel both through sense organs in their hard outer skeleton and with the aid of their antennae.

The sense of hearing is, however, absent, at least in the sense in which we understand it. They have instead a most delicate perception of vibrations which they seem to perceive through special organs termed 'chordotonal organs'. These organs, which are found in the tibia (the last joint but one of the ant's leg), the thorax and the head, are very similar to the better developed 'hearing' organs of the grasshoppers. It has been argued long and often that they *are* hearing organs : that the ants can hear. But this is a matter of extreme doubt which is unsupported by the many experimental tests that have been made. All experts are agreed, however, that they are certainly the organs which tell the ants about the vibrations of the ground to which they are so sensitive. Whether or no they are also organs of hearing, this much is certain. The appreciation of minute vibrations of the earth, or the material of the nest, is a very important warning mechanism. It is this sense which warns the ants of our presence when we make the slightest disturbance of the surface of their nests, or the ground nearby, and brings them scurrying out to aid the defence.

The arguments about ants' hearing can be simply put. The primitive ants have organs in their petioles, or between the first two segments of their gasters, which resemble those of other insects which do produce sound. These organs vary considerably in the detail of their structure, but all consist of a serrated comb, or series of ridges, and a hard point which can be rubbed over it. Furthermore, films have been made which show the ants rubbing the point over the ridge. In only two species is any sound heard when this happens, but then the human range of hearing is very limited. The combs are too small to produce sounds lower than those we hear, but may they not produce sounds belonging to a higher range? The two exceptions to this silence are the African *Megaloponera foetens*, which can be clearly heard, and the American *Pogonomyrmex*, which can also be heard when a sufficient number are enclosed in a glass flask.

Experiments have been made to test if ants of the same and different species will respond to the stridulation of captive individuals, but the results are not satisfactory. The isolation of the captives from the others, who it is claimed responded, have never been sufficiently controlled for there to be any clear interpretation of the result. Against such experiments there must also be set the much more numerous and more careful attempts to discover any response by ants to sounds experimentally produced. These experiments have embraced all manner of insect sound-producing, from the buzzing of flies with fast-moving wings and the scraping of beetles' elytra and ants' bodies to the purely inanimate production of sounds to the highest ranges which experimental whistles are capable of producing. Even at ranges up to 60,000 vibrations per second, far beyond our appreciation, the response is always the same – complete lack of interest. Surely if ants could hear sound they would show some response.

The need for ant hearing felt by some students is largely a need to explain the occurrence of apparent use of these stridulatory organs. Yet in the field, one ant finding honey never calls others to the scene without journeying home; at least the occurrence of such behaviour has never been satisfactorily demonstrated. Although an element of mystery must remain until this matter is more adequately settled, it has little importance to the student of the higher social ants, for they either altogether lack these stridulatory organs (like many *Formicinae*) or possess them only in the most atrophied and useless form. They were evidently therefore of little use to the evolving social ants and played no part in the development of their complex social behaviour and division of labour.

Taking next our own second major sense, that of sight, we find a different and intriguing picture. The range of seeing in the ants is great. How variable it is can be judged by the remarks made in earlier chapters. To avoid confusion only the best of ant vision is considered here. Ants can see colours. Their appreciation of red is rather poorer than ours, but they can see ultra-violet, which to most of us is invisible. For this reason an ultra-violet filter placed over their nests will give them an impression of darkness, while leaving them to us clearly visible and even brightly lit.

Ants can also distinguish between the changes of polarization of light – changes which are quite unappreciable to us. It is certain that ants cannot see clearly: they cannot see a focused image. It seems probable, on the other hand, that the presence of a great number of facets in the compound eyes leads to a better appreciation of movement, since more and more facets will be stimulated as the object moves across the line of vision, thus giving a measured indication of its progress. The function of the simple ocelli is obscure, but may be concerned with close vision, although it has been suggested that they are important in way-finding and in the males and queens in their orientation during flight. This is very uncertain and seems unlikely. Nevertheless, the ants which have well-developed compound eyes – the big ones on the sides of their heads – do find their way almost entirely by sight. The number of facets in these compound eyes varies from one or two to over a thousand. In all the ants with more than thirty or forty facets, sight plays an important part in their orientation. In those with a hundred or more facets, it is the dominant, if not almost the sole, method of way-finding. The light and dark of the sky or the position of the sun are the factors involved. For example, if a wood ant (*F. rufa*) sets out from the nest marching directly towards the sun and, after being allowed to travel sufficiently far to be away from the regular tracks, is captured by being covered with a box, and is then kept in darkness for a period of hours so that the sun has moved to a different angle, it will when released march homewards, not towards the real position of its home, but at an angle. This is because it is now marching almost directly away from the sun at the angle it would have needed to travel to reach home if it had not had to endure a period of darkened captivity. If covered with a transparent box, its sense of orientation is not affected – it travels the right road home.

The sense of taste in ants is developed at least as far as ours. They can distinguish between sweet and bitter, alkaline (or salt) and acid. If they start to eat honey flavoured with substances they dislike– a fact they often fail to appreciate with their antennae – they will at once stop and draw back. And on occasion they will show the utmost discrimination.

Little is known about the ants' sense of touch – they undoubtedly possess minute organs spread over the surface of their bodies, which enable them to appreciate the sensation of being touched or stroked. Indeed, few creatures can obtain so much apparent pleasure from the sensation of being stroked or licked as that evinced by the ants. Their antennae also have organs of touch-perception as well as those for perceiving smell, but little is known about the mechanisms of this sense in the ants.

The sense of balance is well established, but much doubt has been cast by recent experiments into the importance of the ants' appreciation of their sideways movements. That they do have an appreciation of the swings from left to right and right to left made during their travels, is shown by their ability to learn mazes under conditions in which other possible guiding factors are controlled. But it seems that this sense is not especially remarkable as was once thought.

Similarly their sense of distance, of knowing how far they have travelled on either an outward or an inward journey, although undoubtedly developed sufficiently to warn an ant when it has travelled much too far in returning, as it thinks, to the nest, is not in any way especially remarkable. It certainly has not the accuracy of a pedometer, as was once supposed.

There has in the past been too great a tendency to wonderment about the complexities of ant sensation. Their sensory powers are in no way incredible. They differ from ours both in the degree of development of the various senses and in the manner of their sensitivity.

This little homily is stimulated by the credulity of those who would believe that ants have a scent language, or can distinguish smell in solid form. Such beliefs are far beyond the facts now better understood. The ants indeed smell with their feelers and can distinguish smells with a sensitivity difficult for us to appreciate. But their constant tapping of feelers when they meet does not mean that they need a language and that because the feelers are thus visibly employed this language must involve the sense of which they are the organs. It has already been seen that no language is needed to explain the division of labour involved in the daily running of the ant colony. Nor do ants distinguish smells as we do shapes, although many ant students have proposed that the possession of two mobile noses, their antennae, might enable them to do so.

Trail-following by smell is important in a large number of ant species, but it is now accepted that even in those that use this method of way-finding, other factors, such as sight and the appreciation of movement, also play their part. These trails are laid by the periodic touching of the ground with the tip of the gaster. The result is a series of short dashes of scent along the course, often with longish intervals between one another. The ant can follow these on its return or on a further journey. So also can its nest-mates.

It has been suggested that these dashes also indicate the direction of travel – whether the ant is travelling outwards or inwards, and this may well be the case. If so, it is probably a matter of the variation in strength of the scent dash through its brief course that holds the clue, the intensity being stronger at the initial end than at the other where the gaster is about to be withdrawn. Or it may be vice versa. We do not know.

The possession of a two-pronged nose and the manoeuvrability of that organ undoubtedly plays some part in the sensations of the ants. It enables a greater combing of the air to warn of danger or of food. It enables the ant to place the location of any given scent, unattractive or hostile, or attractive and of pleasurable interest, much more exactly than is possible with our crude and single organs. Thus the antennae are used much as a blind man uses his hands, for finding the mouth of a grub and distinguishing it from its back end, and all manner of similar things which we normally achieve by sight. It is in these simple ways that the remarkable nature of this sense is seen. And it is in this manner that the ant world differs so greatly from the glaring cacophonic world that we poor humans have learnt to know too well.

It is at this point well to consider the means by which these various sensations are perceived. The ants, like other insects, have a series of ganglia or nervous masses scattered in a chain down the length of their bodies. These are joined together by a nervous cord which at its forward end, in the head, forms a larger nervous bundle, the brain. From these lower ganglia the nerves run outwards and inwards to and from the many organs of the body – the gut, the muscles, the glands, and sense organs.

If the head of an ant be cut off, it will behave much like a higher animal which has had its cerebrum destroyed, though rather more efficiently. It will stand upright, perhaps quivering slightly, but otherwise immobile. Tweak its leg and it will raise it. Attack it in some other way and a response will be obtained. It cannot feed, but may live some twenty days before it dies, and can even be made to run, though none too well.

The brain of the ant governs its instincts, together with all its more independent behaviour, its learning, and its more problematic insight, the existence or non-existence of which will be discussed more fully in chapter 10.

This brain is different from the other ganglia morphologically as well as in function. This is especially noticeable in the development of the olfactory lobes. Here there are found, as in man, some small pedunculate bodies, small masses of grey matter. These are poorly developed in the male and more highly so in the queens and workers, especially in the latter. Destruction of these bodies alters the whole behaviour of the ant. It loses its powers of memory and the order of its instinctive patterns. Its learning and all its independence of behaviour and its social coherence go by the board. The effect is similar to that which follows the destruction of the middle brain of birds or fishes.

These pedunculate bodies are the great brain of the ants, the governors of all their remarkable behaviour which has led them so far along the road to biological success and the dominance of the insect world.

CHAPTER 6

The Success of the Ants

*

THE chief enemy of an ant is another ant. This is the measure of the ants' success. It is true of only one other living creature – man. The ants cannot claim to be found in every part of the globe like man. But the only regions from which they are absent are the two icebound poles – the Arctic and Antarctic. Until recently they were also absent from Iceland and Greenland, never having had the chance to return to those districts since the last of the Ice Ages, but modern transport and methods of packaging goods have proved an adequate bridge, and ants are now found in both regions. It is this adaptability of the ants to a vast range of climates, coupled with their generally omnivorous appetite and, above all, their developed social life, that has helped to make them so important a factor in the balance of life throughout the globe.

It is surprising how little their importance is realized. In most parts of the world ants are talked of somewhat vaguely as either nuisances or pests, but they are not usually considered to be of major economic importance either as pests or as beneficial insects.

Most people know how vital a part the earthworm plays in aerating the soil and bringing new earth to the surface. Yet how many people realize that in South America, where there are no earthworms, a similar function is performed even more efficiently by the ants? Charles Darwin calculated that over an area of 10,000 square metres (rather more than 2 acres) anywhere in England, the earthworms in the soil would in 100 years bring to the surface from the subsoil 2,598,500 kilograms of earth, the equivalent of about 2,600 tons. In Brazil, equally careful calculations have shown that the total weight of soil brought up from the subsoil to the surface by the ants over the same area and period of time is greater. The ants shift 3,226,250 kilograms of soil each 100 years, or about 3,260 tons; over 600 tons more than the earthworms so highly esteemed by the gardeners. This turning over of the soil is of vital importance wherever the soil is cultivated. Without the constant turning and aeration of the soil plants cannot grow.

What is true of Brazil is obviously true of other tropical countries and to a large extent of most of the temperate regions also, for Brazil possesses no especially unique excavating ants – just the average selection in much the same quantity as in most of the rest of the world. Each colony of our own British Yellow Hill Ant (*Acanthomyops flavus*) will bring up 1 lb. 10 oz. of soil each year, and in North Africa the *Pheidole* working only 100 days a year over an area of 15 sq. yards will move over a ton of soil.

It is this area of the surface soil and the sub-soil immediately below it that is the kingdom of the ants. They may in some countries take to the trees, making them untenable for all except their favoured or tolerated friends, and indeed often do control the fauna of the trees even when they do not actually nest aloft in their trunks or branches. But it is this small surface crust of the globe which is their common home, which they have made their heritage.

The Termites, destructive wood-eating social cockroaches that they are, are confined to the tropics. For the most part they are also limited to a troglodytic, light-fearing existence. The bees and wasps fly in the air and have in consequence a wholly simpler form of life, less full of problems and encounters. Their behaviour reflects this in its comparative simplicity and more stereotyped forms. Their dominance of the land is localized to the confines of their nests and is unimportant, being virtually non-existent.

The number of ant mimics and of lodgers found only in the nests of ants reflects something of their power. Over 5,000 different species of insects and other small living creatures are only found living in association with ants. The comparable figure for the Termites is about the same number of hundreds, two of which are, as has been seen, ants

(p. 105). **This** is amusing, for there is no greater or more successful enemy of the Termites than the ant. Nearly every weapon of defence which the Termites have evolved during their development is specifically directed to aid in the defence against the continuous warfare of the ants. The special large-headed soldier Termites, the unicorn-like horns of the nasute soldiers of *Nasutitermes* through which a special offensive liquid is sprayed, the peculiar mandibles of the *Capritermes* which enable it to spring away from the ants and so make its escape, and the rubbery, latex-like secretions of *Cuptotermes* which stick the jaws of the attacker fast together, are all directed specifically towards their defence against the ants. The ants, on the other hand, are far less concerned with the Termites. They are a most important source of food, but only one source. No ant relies entirely on Termites for its food.

The success of the ants in fighting the termites is enormous and the contribution of this success to the human economy of the tropics must be considerable. The destruction of 80 per cent of the termite colonies of Queensland, South Australia, by the Dolichoderine ant *Iridomyrmex sanguineus*, has already been mentioned (see p. 51). In other tropical countries they are no less effective. The percentage of Termite nests found to be occupied by ants may not be as high as that for *Drepanotermes* and *Hamitermes* in Queensland, but the frequency with which a termite mound turns out to be instead the home of an ant colony is considerable in every region where Termites are found. The most socially developed of the Ponerine ants, *Leptogenys*, march in armies against them, doing immense damage by their depredations. The large Stink Ants, *Megaloponera foetens*, make constant Termite raids, as do the 'Tak' Ants, *Odontomachus*, and the majority of Ponerine ants, whose heavy armour gives little chance of successful defence to the weaker-armed Termites. Formicines, such as *Cataglyphis*, *Prenolepis*, *Polyrhachis*, and many *Camponotus*, take a heavy toll, as do the Dolichoderine *Iridomyrmex* and many Myrmicines, such as *Solenopis geminata* and *Pheidologeton diversus*.

The Success of the Ants

To make a list of Termite-destroying ants would be a vast undertaking, for it would include nearly all the Ponerines, seventy species of which eat Termites as their staple (though not their only) diet, and a majority of the other ants of the tropics. For even the omnivorous ants which herd rather than hunt will not allow the Termites to invade their hunting and herding grounds and the immediate territory around their nests. The war is constant and the carnage immense.

The first recorded European attempts to use ants as pesticides was directed against Termites. In about 1780 Termites were introduced into France, supposedly by ship from San Domingo. At first they did little damage, but by 1829 the matter was becoming serious, for many buildings in Rochefort and La Rochelle were being undermined. One of these was the Prefecture and the other the Arsenal, both official buildings, so that the matter was considered important. It was decided that the Termites might be driven away by introducing some ants into the buildings. Unfortunately the choice of ants was not well made; French ants were used, only to meet the fate they were designed to mete out to the Termites.

It is a common practice in some parts of the East to encourage the ants to live in and around warehouses in order to keep the Termites at bay. In Madras it has for centuries been the custom of the Indians to utilize the Myrmicine ants *Solenopsis geminata* and *Monomorium salomonis* for this purpose. But the Termites are only one amongst many groups of harmful insects that ants destroy.

As early as the thirteenth century A.D. the beneficial qualities of the ants as eradicators of soft-bodied pests were recognized by the Chinese. They reared and protected ants, especially of the Formicine genus *Polyrhachis*, in order to destroy the caterpillars which ravaged their plantations of mandarines and oranges. A special class of labourers, called ant gatherers, was formed to collect the ants from the hills where they abounded and bring them down to the plantations in the plains, where, although present, they were relatively scarce.

The ants were collected by baiting a pig's or goat's bladder with lard and stretching it across the solitary opening of the nest. Liking oily or greasy food, the ants entered the bladders in great numbers, whereupon, after a while, the bladder was closed up and fastened. The ant gatherers then carried them down to the plains and sold them to the orange growers, who let them loose upon their trees. In order to ensure that the ants foraged over every tree, the trees were linked together by bamboo rods, along which the ants could travel from one tree to another. This method was still in use in China as late as the nineteenth century.

The Japanese also made use of ants in a similar manner to control the depredations of a beetle on their mango trees. In Arabia, in the eighteenth century, the Arabs used a species of hill ant to control the serious damage being done to their date palms by another species of ant!

One of the worst pests of the cotton industry is the notorious Cotton Boll Weevil, which causes over 120 million dollars' worth of damage to the cotton crop each year. All other methods having failed, this pest is kept in check by the encouragement of a dozen species of ants, which destroy more than 50 per cent of the weevil's larvae.

In the temperate northern regions of the world, the Wood Ants play a vital part in protecting the woodlands from the destructive attacks of many beetle larvae and other pests. Since they destroy between 50,000 and 100,000 insects each day, their presence or absence in the woods and forests is of some importance. This was recognized in Northern Germany many years ago, and in 1880 a Prussian law was passed protecting them from interference. A new law to replace the older one which had fallen into abeyance was passed in 1936 and is still enforced. The French forest lands and some British ones have suffered severely because of the depredations of the ants' egg collectors, who disturb the wood ants' nests to obtain the pupae for food for domesticated fish. During the last fourteen years, many experiments on the artificial breeding, rearing, and introduction of the Wood Ants into new areas have been undertaken in both

Britain and Germany, especially in the latter country. And methods have now been established which have shown a high degree of success.

One of the most amusing attempts to use ants as a pesticide was that tried out by the British Government in Ceylon early in the last century. The Coffee Bug, *Lecanium coffeae*, was at that time proving more than usually devastating in its attacks, and it was decided to try and control it with the aid of the Red Weaver Ant (*Oecophylla smaragdina*). All went extremely well. The ants were introduced and, Chinese fashion, the trees were joined together by rods. The ants ate the bug and indeed nearly wiped it out. The trouble started, and the experiment hurriedly ended, when the natives tried to tend the trees, for their oily skins proved just as attractive to the ants as the insects they were supposed to destroy. The natives threatened to stop work and leave the estates, and the experiment had to be abandoned.

The importance of the Pseudomyrmine and Dolichoderine ants in protecting the *Tillandsia* and *Acacia* plants in which they nest is a small matter compared to the dependence of the cocoa plants of the Gold Coast on ants of the genus *Crematogaster*. More than half the cocoa plants (*Theobroma lesiocarpa*) are pollinated by these ants, and if the ants are inactive, as when the weather is dry, the rate of pollination falls abruptly. Although in this field of usefulness the ants cannot rival the bees, there can be little doubt that, especially in the tropics, they are important agents of pollination.

But success is not to be confused with beneficence to man. The sheer biological success of the ants is to be judged by the sum total of all their effects upon the life of the world and not just by those which are beneficial to man's idea of the world's economy. The mixing and aeration of the soil, the destruction of termites and a myriad other noxious insects, are only one side of the story; a side, it is true, which is worthy of greater consideration than is usually accorded to it.

The numbers of ant guests and the number of other insects not strictly ant guests, but with which the ants associate and which they protect, is perhaps the greatest of all indications of the ants' success. The seeking of patronage and protection implies the possession of power by those from whom these things are sought. The evolution of 5,000 species of camp followers is no small achievement for a group that itself only numbers around 15,000 species, many of which are poor relics, with little protection and few rewards to dispense.

It is in the large societies of the Social ants and, to a lesser extent, those of the nomadic Dorylines, that these protégés, both evil and good, are found. For many of them give the ants little enough reward for the protection gained from their societies, and others are parasites and secret robbers. But that is the fate of the powerful of all kinds.

These guests, or 'myrmecophiles', as they are called, belong to nearly every class of insect and to other groups of the Arthropods as well. There are spiders and silver fish, aphids (greenflies and blackflies), mites, and a multitude of beetles.

The spiders provide some of the best ant mimics, especially those like *Mimanomma* and *Mimeciton*, which not only copy the colour of the African *Dorylus* and *Eciton* army ants with which they live, but also the very manner of their walking, the six legs, the upward feelers and, in the case of *Mimanomma*, the very joints of the petiole and post-petiole, and the formation of the gaster.

These spiders gain the smell of the ants and are tolerated by them, feeding on the booty which they capture, dismember, but fail to eat. Their style of walking, shape, and colour protects them from the hungry jaws of birds, reptiles, and frogs, which, misled by their mimicry, leave them alone. Nearly all the species of the European Beetle genus *Atemeles* mimic ants. They even mimic the solicitous tapping of the feelers by which one ant requests food from another – and succeed in obtaining it. The strange small Hymenopteron, *Gonatopus*, is another mimic which lives with species of *Myrmica* and *Formica*, but gains only the protection of the nest from which it sallies forth to attack and eat small Homopteron bugs.

Most of the guests that do not belong to the ant herds mimic them to some degree, however slight, if only in their movements or in the reflections given off by their body in the light. Many beetles belonging to the fauna of the ants' nests like *Lomechusa* look totally unlike the ants on close examination. But uncover a nest and you will find them difficult to spot. Their concave-sided thorax and rolled-up gaster reflect the light in such a way that they appear thin-thoraxed and small and round-gastered. These creatures are real parasites, feeding on the grubs and eggs of ants, and are especially common in the nests of the Blood-Red Slave-makers (*Formica sanguinea*). Yet even they need to seem ant-like: not to deceive the ants, for we must not forget theirs is a world of smell, not of sight. No, it is to deceive the other creatures which might otherwise prey on them, but which, because they seem ant-like, leave them alone. How precious this quality must be to draw forth so much copying! Evolution is not famed for flattery. Rigorous selection is its rule. Yet, apart from the mimics and the actual residents of the ants' nests, and companions on their trails, there is a vast host of parasites almost equally dependent. Flies like *Bengalia depressus* steal food by diving on their marching columns and others like *Microdon* live part of their life in their nests. But then so also does the Blue Butterfly, *Lycaena arion*, whose caterpillar life was long a mystery until this was discovered.

Mites without number abound on the surface of their nests, seeming to find conditions better there than in their more isolated and originally more natural habitat. Many of these mites are not dependent, occurring frequently apart from the ants, but certainly they gain much benefit if the high population in the nests and in their vicinity is any indication. They are quite distinct and must not be confused with the actual mite parasites of ants: mites which live on their bodies, hanging to the sides of their head, thorax, and gaster. These and other bodily parasites of ants are a separate army, including flies whose grubs, hatching from eggs laid on the ants' heads, eat slowly into their brains, and a number of nematode worms which play a similar part to our own tapeworms. There are special fungi which attack ants, eating into their bodies and, no doubt, legions of equally specialized bacteria and viruses, for the diseases of ants are many, and, it may be added, most difficult to treat.

The ant cattle are, however, the most important of all the ant guests to the ants, and they are also the worst as far a man is concerned. The story of the ant cattle is one of the most remarkable of all animal stories. The greenflies, black-flies and other aphids and the coccids or scale insects, who are the 'cows' of the ants, receive fully as much attention as their bovine counterparts. They are taken out to pasture, brought in again to the shelter of the nest. They are guarded while they are out and are further protected by the shelters built for them by the ants. Their eggs are carefully looked after in the nest until they hatch out, and species preferring to live underground are pastured out on the roots of plants in and around the nest. That patch of bare lawn in the garden may well be due to a colony of Yellow Lawn Ants, *Acanthomyops mixtus*, living underneath it and pasturing their large aphid herds upon the roots of the grass. The ants of this species never appear above ground in day-time, neither do their cattle.

The milk the ants obtain from these insects is the honey dew which forms their excreta. Normally the aphids and coccids squirt this out at random when they are not attended by ants, but when the ants herd them they only release it when the ants milk them. This milking process consists of a gentle stroking of the 'cow' with the ants' feelers. After a few seconds of this soothing treatment the aphid (or coccid) slowly exudes its honey-dew. In the aphids this is done through the two hooks which stick out and slightly upwards at the hind end of the abdomen. The ant which is milking the aphid hurriedly licks up the drops of fluid, and some-times strokes a bit longer to see if it can obtain some more, and then hurries off to the next of its cows.

The majority of the Formicine ants keep such insect herds, especially *Acanthomyops*, in the temperate regions, which is almost entirely dependent on them for its food supply, and the genera *Paratrechina, Prenolepis,* and to a lesser extent *Camponotus,* of the tropical and sub-tropical regions. Most Dolichoderines also milk these coccids and aphides and sometimes herd them, especially the tropical genus *Dolichoderus,* while the Myrmicine genera *Cremato-gaster* and *Pheidole* are notorious in Africa for their fierce protection and harmful encouragement and herding of scale insects. Other Myrmicines, such as *Monomorium* and some *Solenopsis,* are almost equally bad offenders. Although the ants of the other ant sub-families (except the Dorylines) may feed on the sweet excreta of these insects when they encounter them on their foraging expeditions, especially the *Pseudomyrmīnae,* none of them keeps aphid or coccid herds. This behaviour is confined to the Social Ants.

The power of the ants lies in their numbers, their comparative longevity, which makes possible their stable colonial form of life, and their wide geographical distribution. There are more ants in the world than all other terrestrial animals combined. They are found wandering inside desert borders and in the oases. They are found on the sea-shores and deep within the largest forests. They are found high up in the highest mountains. The race *lochmatteri* of the Eurasian Black Bog Ant (*Formica picca*) has been recorded at 15,740 feet in the Himalayas. Ants are found in the houses of man. In 1852 it was said that every single house in Funchal, capital of Madeira, had its colony of *Pheidole mega-cephala.* To-day most houses there still have their 'House Ants', but now the dreaded Argentine Ant, *Iridomyrmex humilis,* has replaced the *Pheidole.* Ants are found in quantity nesting on every ocean liner. They are found foraging round the debris pushed along by the prows of Nile steamers. They are found within the Arctic Circle around the northern coast of the U.S.S.R. and at North Cape in Norway. In the tropics plagues of ants are not unknown. In 1760 it was seriously debated whether the island of Barbados should be abandoned, because of the sudden and disastrous appearance of a plague of 'Fire Ants,' *Solenopsis geminata.* Their large aphid and scale insect herds did such damage to the sugar-cane crops that the island, formerly a flourishing colony, was driven to the verge of bankruptcy.

The same ants appeared in Martinique in 1763, the year after its capture from the French by the British Admiral Rodney. Seven years later the island of Grenada, 170 miles to the south, suffered a similar fate. The numbers of the ants were so immense that the roads were entirely covered by them for miles on end. When horses travelled over them the impressions of their feet remained visible only for a moment or two before being filled up by the surrounding masses. The Government offered a reward of £20,000 for the desstruction of the ants, but all attempts were unavailing until Nature came to their aid and a tornado of great violence swept a large part of the multitude out to sea.

H. W. Bates in his famous book, *The Naturalist on the Amazons*, records how, when he visited Aveyros, a settlement forty miles from Itaituba on the Tapajos tributary of the Amazons, he found the soil of the whole village undermined by the galleries of these Fire Ants (*Solenopsis geminata*). 'The houses are overrun with them; they dispute every fragment of food with the inhabitants and destroy clothing for the sake of the starch. All eatables were obliged to be suspended in baskets from the rafters, and the cords well soaked with copaüba balsam, which is the only known means of preventing them from climbing.' A few years before Bates's visit (in 1852) Aveyros had been deserted for a space of several years on account of this small red dreaded 'formiga da fogo' with its burning sting.

The Fire Ant has now spread far beyond its Amazonian home, travelling by ship throughout the warmer regions of the world. But even *Solenopsis geminata* is not so ubiquitous and so disdainful of man's presence as the minute Myrmicine, Pharaoh's Ant (*Monomorium pharaonis*), lord of the ocean-going ants, and dominant on nearly every ocean steamer. Its special domain, apart from ships, is houses, where once it is established it is wellnigh impossible to eradicate. It needs some warmth, but can survive amazing variations of temperature. Moreover, its colonies may number between two and three million individuals with over two thousand queens. Its favourite nesting place is under the kitchen floor, but small incipient colonies have even been found in the handle of a table-knife and in the scabbard of a sword, which was kept hanging on the wall as a trophy. The author was once sent a living worker which was found in the very centre of a newly-baked loaf of bread. How it got there remains a mystery, since it scarcely seems possible that it could have survived the heat of baking.

The *Formicinae* also have their cosmopolitan species. Chief among them is the small black long-legged *Prenolepis longicornis*, second only to *M. pharaonis* in the extent of its spread and its haunting of human buildings. If *M. pharaonis* is the lord of the ships, then *P. longicornis* is the lord of the greenhouses throughout the world, and its first cousin, *P. vividula*, runs it close.

Many of the social ants do not take kindly to the close proximity of man. The wood ants soon move away from the immediate neighbourhood of new housing sites, and will only be found nesting in the largest of gardens.

Acanthomyops is, however, more adaptable. The Black Lawn Ant, *A. niger*, and the Jet-Black Ant (*A. fuliginosus*) take little note of human interference with their surroundings as long as their nests and food supply remain unharmed. The Black Lawn Ant would almost seem to welcome it, to judge by the speed with which it learns that the foundations of houses provide a most solid protection for their nests, and that nearby within the edifice there is often a goodly, if at times irregular, new source of food. Unlike the house ants, *Acanthomyops niger* never nest within the house. They forage for food within by entering through the door or window. Their nest may be around and even under the foundations, but always near the edges, where they give way to gravelled paths or garden.

The garden provides another benefit to other species. In Europe it is the particular perquisite of the Yellow Lawn Ant (*A. umbratus*). True, *A. niger* is its rival. But in an open competition the troglodyte yellow ant always wins. This little Yellow Formicine was long thought to be rather a rare species, when in fact it is one of the most abundant of European Ants, especially in Britain. The reason for this error is a simple one from which a lesson may profitably be learnt. The Yellow Lawn Ant lives a completely subterranean existence. Only when the marriage flight takes place, or when it is the host species in a Jet Black Ant – Yellow Lawn Ant mixed colony (see p. 103), are its workers ever seen above the ground. It does in fact appear above the surface in the darkness of the warm summer nights, but disappears below at once if caught in the beam of a torch.

Other troglodytic species of ants may be noticed when their nests are disturbed by digging, or if, like the Yellow Hill Ant (*A. flavus*), they build a hillock; not so the Yellow Lawn Ant. Its preference for nesting under grass swards or turf makes such discovery rare. After all, who habitually digs up his lawn, and how frequently is the sward of the downs and forestland disturbed?

Unseen myriads of ants unthought of by man exist above, beside his doorstep, and under the ground over which he daily walks. There must be many tropical species thought equally rare, which in fact are just as widespread and just as populous – for a large colony of these unsuspected Yellow Lawn Ants may cover an area of between 100 and 200 square feet and contain a million workers and a thousand queens. It is probable that some thousand species of ants, many of them social Formicines or Myrmicines, exist as yet undiscovered because of their dislike of light and their ability to maintain themselves by subterranean hunting, or the keeping of subterranean herds. As with other insects, a yellow colour is the hallmark of the troglodytes, for wholly yellow ants seem little able to withstand the direct rays of the sun.

The persistence of the ants in the face of all manner of assaults is in due part to their physical stamina – their immense persistence in living. They are difficult creatures to kill, except by poison. In Tunisia in the eighteenth century the Arabs found it simplest to use another species of ant to kill those which were menacing their prosperity by destroying their palm trees. Before the advent of modern insecticides such methods of ant-killing were often the best.

Something of the tenacity of life of an individual ant can be gathered from their ability to survive both starvation and drowning, the ability of the worker ants of many species to survive for periods of six or seven weeks without being fed, and the queens for even longer periods. Worker ants of *Camponotus castaneus* and *Formica subsericea* have survived periods of experimental starvation of between fourteen and fifteen weeks !

Perhaps even more astonishing is the ability of many ants to resist drowning. It might be thought that flooding was the one great danger to the ant colony – a danger against which they have no defence. This is not the case. For one thing, many ants can survive long periods under water. To place an ant under water for an hour or so, or even for half a day, will rarely kill it. Most ants can survive twenty-four hours under water and be none the worse for their adventure at the end of it. There are many records of ants surviving a full week's submergence and living a normal span of two or more years after the event.

When faced with floods, ants will often take active steps to ensure their safety and that of their brood. They form a nest-ball, similar to that made by the Doryline Army ants (p. 87), in which the ants themselves are the nest material, and the spaces between their bodies the nest passages. Then, with brood and queens safely enclosed in the centre of the living sphere, they float on the surface of the waters until dry land is reached. I once received such a nest-ball of a small *Monomorium* from Palestine composed entirely of dead ants. The ants had been placed in the water meant to kill them before it reached a high enough temperature to do so, and before being floated apart had managed to form a typical nest-ball. When boiling water was poured over it they died, still clinging to each other with queens and brood enclosed inside.

That the *Monomorium* remained together while they died

does not seem surprising when it is remembered that ants habitually fight to the death, never letting go of their enemy. It is not uncommon to see ants wandering about the nest, or going out foraging after a battle with the heads of their dead enemies still fastened to their feelers or their legs. This characteristic of the ants has been utilized in many countries of the tropics. Living ants are made to bite together the two sides of a wound, then the rest of the body is broken off and the head (or series of heads) remains to form a primitive surgical stitch.

The widespread success of the ants has in the past caused them to be used by man for a variety of purposes. The natives of Australia and of South America commonly ate them. Even to-day the honey ants of Australia and South America with their swollen repletes (p. 88) are, as has been mentioned, considered a special delicacy and often served alive on a special dish at wedding feasts. The banqueters pick each ant up by the head and thorax and, holding it in their fingers, bite off the gaster with its large honey-filled crop. They are said to be very tasty.

The formic acid of the Wood Ants is an old-established remedy for rheumatism. The recipe is simple. Boil up a small sackful of wood ants (*Formica rufa*) in a pailful of water. Add the liquid to your bath, straining off the ants and debris as you pour it in. Placing your foot in the nest of one of the stinging Myrmicine species of ants used to be thought a cure for gout. It is said to be still practised in some parts of Africa.

In Victorian days a potion distilled from ants (species unnamed) was said to be an excellent cure for roaring in the ears or 'the vapours'. And it is still the practice in some parts of Scandinavia to use a concoction of the acid of the Formicine ants (usually of Wood Ants) as a flavouring for cakes, or for the sugar icing. Another less worthy use is the distilling of ants along with rye to give a flavour to the cheaper kinds of brandy.

Several kinds of tropical ants are used as flavourings in a dried and powdered form, while the Sewing Tree Ant

(*Oecophylla smaragdina*) is still commonly pounded into a paste in Burma, Siam, and parts of India and used as a condiment.

Unless you have caught your ants, all these recipes are, of course, as tantalizing as those of Mrs Beeton, which start by telling the long-suffering housewife to 'take a dozen eggs . . .' The catching of ants can be quite an art, as will be seen from the next chapter.

CHAPTER 7

How to Collect Ants and how to Study them

*

THE main difficulty in collecting ants is finding the particular kind you want. The second difficulty is to find the nest of the ants of which you have perhaps found a solitary worker, or a few individual hunters. The third difficulty is to find the queens within the nest, and the fourth to catch one of them. The problems of packing and porterage are slight compared with the practice of these arts, for such they are. Likewise, making an observation nest is a simple matter compared to the art of keeping colonies of ants in a thriving, healthy condition over a period of years.

To start at the beginning : it is quite easy to find workers of the commonest ant in the district, as long as you know its habits. It is usually quite easy even if you don't know its habits, although if it happens to be a troglodyte species it may, like *Acanthomyops umbratus* mentioned in the last chapter, be overlooked. It frequently is very difficult to find the nest of an ant whose multitudes cover the ground. The trails of the social ants do form a guide to the searcher – they are more frequented nearer home. On the other hand, most trail-forming ants make temporary resting sites – half-way houses – along their routes, and these can easily be mistaken for the actual nest. If the nest is surmounted by a hillock, like those of the European *Formica rufa* and *A. flavus*, or is suspended like a Chinese lantern from the branch of a tree like the nests of the Spiny Tree Ants (*Polyrhachis*) and Spinning Tree Ants (*Oecophylla*) of Australia and Asia, then again the search is simplified. It is when the nest is just 'in the earth' or under the bark of a tree that the art of ant collecting is really needed. But in many cases it may be needed before this for the finding of the first individual workers. To the really experienced collector there is little difference between this event and the finding of the nest, for it is the nest that he goes for at once, without any preliminary scrubbing around.

It is well-nigh impossible to give in these few pages a comprehensive guide to the finding of ants. Nevertheless, there are a few golden rules that will be found to apply throughout the world. The first of these has already been mentioned. It states quite simply that Ponerine ants never nest anywhere but in the earth. Therefore don't turn over hillocks for them, or search for them under the bark of living trees. Look under stones or logs, or twigs, or in small crannies in the earth. The second general law states that ants like the warmth. Look for them in the places having a southern aspect; whether it be south-east or south-west is irrelevant, as long as there is a southern element in the aspect of the direct rays of the sun. Do not forget in considering this problem that the ants' world is a microcosm compared to ours. While a large hillside facing south is an ants' paradise, an area of a few square feet or yards on a different slope may equally be favourable. Such a spot may well be a good place to seek the nests of the smaller species and those which live in less populous colonies and do not need a large foraging area.

In a sense this is merely a part of the third rule of ant-hunting – look and consider before you start searching. If you are searching for all the species in a locality, then you should obtain a good idea of the possibilities from this preliminary inspection. Walk round the area and decide what kinds of ants you are likely to find, and where they are likely to be nesting. This preliminary inspection is even more important when the search is for a particular species. A record that a certain ant has been found in a locality rarely gives exact details of the spot.

Rule four says that an ants' nest is usually at some sort of focal spot in any given landscape. It is not just placed at random in the middle of an area of similar ground. It is in an ants' nest type of spot. Each piece of ground will be found to have spots that, after some experience in ant-hunting, can be recognized as likely places. For example loose stones, however small (but never of immense size), which are embedded in the ground, provide such focal points. The heat is absorbed by the stone and helps to warm the nest. The stone also gives protection. Small pieces of wood, or rotting tree trunks and tufts of grass or moss, or slabs of moss in an even area of soil, are all focal points. Slight elevations in the soil surface, and slight indentations or corners in a bank, are similar foci. Remember the nest must never, however much the ant species loves dampness, become utterly waterlogged. Put yourself in fact in the ants' place and pick the best site you can see to hand. It is amazing how successful this method of ant-hunting can be.

The actual nests of ants are a separate study and are discussed later, but a simplified guide to the types of places to find different types of ants is given in the key (see pp. 140-1).

Equipment for ant collecting should be as simple as possible. The main items needed are a trowel for digging (a spade will also be necessary in the case of large colonies of the social ants); one large cotton or linen sheet, or, alternatively, a large sheet of white paper (two whole sheets of newspaper will do in an emergency); a stout knife for cutting roots or opening up a nest enclosed in a tree stump or a twig; two or three dozen glass tubes about 3 inches long and half an inch in diameter (small medicine bottles or tablet boxes or tins will do almost as well if they are clean and dry); a small quantity of cotton-wool; two or three sacks, together with some string, and a small quantity of jam jars with lids are also useful. Killing bottles are not a good idea for use with ants. It is much better to fill some of the 3-inch tubes with a solution of hydrochloric acid and alcohol. Both these chemicals are easily obtainable at the local chemist's in most countries and should cost only a shilling or so altogether. The alcohol should be of 50 per cent strength. To make the killing solution, dilute the hydrochloric acid to half its strength and mix it with the alcohol in the proportion of one-third dilute acid to two-thirds 50 per cent alcohol. The ants will die fairly quickly when placed in this solution and will not become set – i.e. brittle and with their limbs in fixed positions – if they are left in it for a few days. They should not, however, be left in the killing mixture for more than a week. Several different lots of ants can be placed in each tube of killing mixture if they are separated by a small wad of cotton-wool. In each case a pencilled note of the place, date, and, if possible, rough identification, should be placed in the tube with each lot of ants. If the compartments thus made are also numbered, then a number on the paper slip will enable a quick correlation to be made between the specimens and detailed notes entered in your field note-book.

Some of the glass tubes will be needed for small colonies of living ants or for queen ants. Never put living ants in a glass tube, or indeed in any container without some earth or nest materials. Always place the queens of the Social Myrmicine, Dolichoderine, or Formicine ants in a separate tube from the workers. If the workers and brood are in a sack or jam jar, place the queens in tubes, and do not put more than two or three queens in a single tube. Don't forget that the queens, also, need earth or nest materials in the tube. If you collect more than one colony of any particular species of ant, take especial care to ensure that you have marked the tubes containing the queens, and the jars, bags, or tubes containing the colonies carefully so that there is no possibility of confusion. The wrong queen introduced into the wrong captive colony often leads to the killing of the queen. This applies just as much to the various colonies of a commune as to the different nests of the non-commune-making species.

Never place Formicine ants in glass containers. If this is absolutely unavoidable, make sure there is more than ample wood or earth in the tubes. The reason for this is the danger of their killing themselves by squirting their own acid over themselves. Even without squirting they tend to become covered with acid when enclosed in a small space with an insufficiency of absorbent material. It is difficult to squash ants, so the risk of jamming a tube tight with earth and twigs is less than that of leaving the ants too free and with too little absorbent material.

If live ants are being collected, the first task when the nest is located is to find the queen. The sheet is carried for this purpose. Dig up the nest as completely as possible, paying special attention to the nooks and crannies near roots, or buried stones. If the nest has a mound above it, turn it over on to the sheet before digging, and do a rapid inspection for queens and brood. Fill a jam jar or two with brood if they are in the heap, but don't spend more than a minute on this cursory search. Reverse the sheet so that it covers the mound material and dig for dear life, placing the material excavated on the sheet. If carried, the spade may come in useful here, both in turning over the heap (if present) and in digging out the nest. Often it is useless, because of the tendency of ants to build their nests around the roots of trees and shrubs.

When most of the ants have been removed on to the sheet, the inspection proper can begin. A queen must be found, or the colony will be of little value and should be returned as far as possible to its nest site so that the hiding queens can return to their worker colleagues.

The queens may be found during the excavation. They may be found before it is begun in the case of an ant like *Myrmica*, which often nests under stones, being exposed to view as soon as the stone cover is removed. If a queen is not found in the material on the sheet all is not lost, for one or more queens may very well have taken shelter under the sheet! Or they may have been in the mound material all the time – more usually this is not the case, unless it is near the time of the marriage flight or on a hot spring day. The whole point of turning over the mound material bodily and after a quick search placing the sheet on top of it was to provide an especially convenient hiding-place for the queens. If there is no mound, then the sheet should be placed right beside and almost overlapping the site of the excavation.

It is easy to pick up the ants with one's fingers, but some people prefer to use forceps. For handling live ants a cheap pair of eyebrow tweezers are as good as the most expensive scientific implement. Better still, be brave and use your fingers. The ant is less likely to get hurt and will at the same time get used to being handled and will learn to recognize your odour. Both forceps and fingers are impossible in the case of the very small ants. A different method must be used. This is the insufflator. The insufflator is a tube of glass corked at both ends. Smaller glass tubes are inserted into both corks and pushed through so that they extend beyond the cork both inside the larger tube and outside. The inside end of one of the tubes is then covered with a piece of gauze and a piece of rubber tubing is attached to the outside end of the same small tube. The ants can then be sucked up by the collector in perfect safety, the gauze preventing the ants being pulled up the rubber tube into his mouth. The extension of the other glass tube at, as it might be termed, the ants' nest end of the tube, inside the larger glass cylinder, makes it difficult for the ants which have been sucked up to find their way out again.

Just as there are two reasons why ants are collected, so there are two things which can be done with them on the return of the collector to his home or laboratory. If the ants are collected for observation purposes, then the appropriate apparatus must be manufactured. If they are collected as dead material for study, then they must be mounted, set, and identified.

In the latter case they must be taken out of the killing mixture within the week, and placed in solutions of plain alcohol. If they are to be set at once they need only be washed in it, but they can safely be left in the 50 per cent alcohol for long periods. Setting the larger ants is not a difficult task. The ants are taken out of the tube of alcohol and placed on a sheet of blotting paper, or other drying paper. While drying, the feelers and legs should be extended to more or less natural positions. Leave the ants for a few hours and then mount them on a small square of card or Perspex. Use only two small blobs of glue under the thorax and gaster. If possible use gum tragacanth, but most of the cellulose proprietary brands are quite adequate substitutes, if this is not available. Make out a separate card of similar size bearing the relevant data and mount both the cards on the same pin. The ant should be on top, near the top of the pin and the card bearing the data farther down the shank of the pin. Special entomological pins should be used, since they are specially treated to make them resistant to rust and verdigris. They are also longer. Such pins can be bought quite easily from any dealer in scientific equipment. Several ants from the same colony may be mounted on a single card.

The smaller ants are better mounted at the end of cardboard or Perspex points. It is possible to set even the smallest ant, or, for that matter, to dissect out its gizzard, but it is rarely done and needs a steady hand. Cut out a cardboard or Perspex triangle and mount the ant close to the apex with a blob of glue under its thorax. Then proceed as before, mounting on a pin with the data on a separate card below.

Making observation nests for keeping ants in captivity is not as difficult a matter as it sounds. There are two simple types that anyone can make. The first kind consists of two sheets of glass, oblong in shape and from 8 to 16 inches in length by 4 to 8 inches in width, separated by a plaster of Paris wall. This plaster wall is in the form of a figure 8 which is not quite closed at the waist. To make it, take one of the sheets of glass and lay it flat on a bench, or on the kitchen table. Then get between two and four pounds of *builder's* plaster of Paris – *not* the fine medical kind, nor some proprietary mixture – just plain greyish builder's plaster of Paris. The coarseness of its texture is healthier for the ants. Mix a quantity of this in a bowl and with it draw the two-chambered figure of 8 design on the sheet of glass, leaving the centre part which forms the chambers clear of plaster. Lay the plaster fairly thickly, say, about half-an-inch to an inch wide and about half an inch deep. Soap the second sheet of glass and squeeze it down on top of the plaster until there are no gaps left in the wall through which the ants could escape. All that then remains to be done is to leave the plaster to set, which should take about a quarter of an hour or twenty minutes. Then clean the top glass thoroughly and wipe round the bottom glass. Do not remove the wall from the bottom glass sheet, but break off any obviously weak bits of plaster. The ants can be placed in one of the chambers and food in the other one, and any part of the nest can be easily opened merely by sliding the top sheet of glass. The part which is to be used as the nest should be covered with a sheet of cardboard when the ants are not being watched.

The second type of observation nest is also made of plaster of Paris, but is more complicated in form. To make it take a sheet of glass about 12 inches long and 7 inches wide. Place it on a metal tray or on another larger sheet of glass. Build a wall of plasticine round the glass sheet (the 12 by 7 sheet which is to form the roof of the nest). Make this wall about one inch high and be sure that it is firmly stuck to the base, i.e. to the tray or larger sheet of glass. Then, on top of the glass which is to be the roof of the nest, make a plasticine mould of its chambers and passages. These should be about a quarter of an inch high. It is best to make one square or oblong outer chamber at one end of the glass and a long single passage leading from this to the rest of the nest. The arrangement of the latter can be as simple or as complex a maze of chambers and passages as you wish. When the mould is completed pour in the plaster of Paris and leave it to dry. After it is dry, say, after half an hour, remove the wall and turn the nest over. Take off the glass and remove the plasticine mould of the passages and chambers.

When making the wall round the glass roof it is wise to place one end of it flush with the glass, but leave a space of about half an inch between it and the glass around the rest of the perimeter. If this is done, it will be possible to slide the glass roof off the nest when it is completed, there being no barrier to prevent this at the end where the wall was built flush with the glass, while the other half-inch plaster edges keep the glass properly in position. A further improvement can be made by cutting the glass roof across the top of the outer chamber – the square or oblong chamber which is separated from the rest of the nest.

The small slip of glass at the end of the nest, covering half this chamber, can then be removed, or slid back, thus enabling the ants to be fed without the nest proper being disturbed. Both these types of plaster nest can be made either larger or smaller than the size given. These sizes are, however, the convenient average size for most medium-sized ants.

Some kinds of ants need more space than is provided by these nests. Ants which habitually travel long distances on their foraging expeditions must be given the chance to undertake similar journeys when they are kept in captivity. The simplest method of overcoming this difficulty, while avoiding the manufacture of very large and heavy plaster nests, is to insert two pieces of glass tube into the sides of the nest while it is being manufactured. The entrance and exit to the ordinary observation nest thus formed can then be connected to a series of runways made of tubing. It is well to make them lead somewhere, say, to a corked-up collecting tube or jam jar, the tubes of the runway being inserted through the cork of the collecting tube to enable the ants both to enter the vessel and to return from it. The cork prevents the ants from escaping and the jam jar or tube becomes part of a closed foraging circuit. The placing of food in this vessel helps to complete the illusion.

A few ants, like the wood ants (*Formica* species), cannot be kept in plaster nests with safety because of the glass roof. There is danger of their acid dripping from it on top of them, if they become excited and start squirting it – as they may well do if they see that they are being watched. Such ants are best kept in an ordinary zinc caterpillar breeding-cage, with a zinc door at the back and a glass window in front.

The making of the observation nest is only the beginning of ant-keeping. The ants must be fed and the temperature and humidity must be kept within reasonable bounds. A tropical ant will need considerable warmth and a moister atmosphere than a British ant. A few more golden rules can well be taken to heart. The most important of these is never to disturb your ants too often. Don't keep on taking the cardboard off the nest proper and then putting it back a few minutes later, only to repeat the process in another five minutes' time. The cardboard can be kept off for long periods if wanted; it is the constant alteration of light and dark that causes trouble. Leave them alone as much as possible ; even when feeding them and moistening the plaster.

A really large colony of omnivorous ants, say, Wood Ants or Doryline Army Ants, will need a great deal of food. Army Ants do need feeding every day, but Wood Ants should be fed not more than twice a week. Feeding once a week is quite often enough for most ants. Uneaten food goes bad, be it insect flesh or honey, and ants can survive a paucity of food a great deal better than the invasion of mould. Uneaten honey ferments and causes drunkenness; if there is old honey in the feeding-place, don't be too hasty to remove seemingly dead workers nearby – they may merely be dead drunk. If there is water in a watch-glass inside the nest, the ants will often throw these drunken companions into the water, whereupon they soon recover. But this is not purposeful: they will often throw truly dead ants into it as well.

Moisture is supplied by the damping of the plaster of Paris. A watch-glass containing water can be placed in the nest, but is unnecessary. In summer the plaster of Paris of the nest should be thoroughly dampened once each week. In winter it should be moistened once every ten, twelve, or fourteen days, according to the dryness of the plaster. *Do not do it more often.* But, when doing it, do it thoroughly. Once a quarter – every three months – the ants should be removed from the nest and the plaster and glass should be scrubbed clean with soapy water. Be careful to rinse both glass and plaster carefully before replacing the ants.

Food can be a problem, for ants have their fads which vary *ad infinitum* from species to species. In the main soft-bodied insects and/or honey or syrup fill the bill. Don't use jam, because it goes mouldy too quickly. Do not, repeat *do not*, give too much food. A thousand *Formica rufa* will need about half a pint of insects each week as food. A colony of five thousand Jet Black Ants (*Acanthomyops fuliginosus*) or Black Lawn Ants (*A. niger*) will need about two large teaspoonfuls of honey each week. A colony of five hundred

HABITAT			TROPICAL	
Bogs Swamps Rotted Wood	*Damp-loving and Dark-loving*		Cerapachyinae Ponerinae	
	Damp-loving and Light-loving		Camponotus and some other Formicinae Some Myrmicinae The larger Ponerinae	
Soil (neither extremely dry nor extremely damp)	*Dark-loving*	*Hillock-making* *No mound*	Ponerinae Myrmicinae A few Dorylinae	
	Light-loving	*Hillock-making* *No mound*	Myrmicinae, e.g. Pheidole and Solenopsis Formicinae Some Dolichoderinae, e.g. Dolichoderus	
Very dry soils	*Heath or Savanna* *Desert* *Semi-arid areas*		Formicinae, e.g. Camponotus Myrmicinae (including Harvesting Ants)	
Forest Woodland	*Nesting in Tree*		Pseudomyrminae (*except* Pachysima rufonigra) Many Dolichoderinae, e.g. Azteca Some Formicinae, e.g. Colobopsis Polyrhachis Oecophylla	
	Nesting on ground		Ponerinae Cerapachyinae Myrmicinae Formicinae Dorylinae	
Cosmo-politan	*Only in human habitations*			
	In countryside as well		Solenopsis geminata Iridomyrmex humilis Monomorium pharaonis Pheidole megacephala Prenolepis sp. Odontomachus haematodes	
Mountains (*over 6,500 feet*)			Formica Acanthomyops Prenolepis Acantholepis	Polyrhachis Cataglyphis Camponotus Plagiolepis Formicinae

CLIMATE

SUB-TROPICAL	TEMPERATE	
Cerapachyinae Ponerinae	Ponerinae	
Camponotus and some other Formicines Some Myrmicines The larger Ponerinae	Leptothorax and a few other Myrmicinae Formica picea	
Formicinae Ponerinae Some Myrmicinae Leptanillinae	Formicinae, e.g. Acanthomyops Ponerinae Some Myrmicinae	
Formicinae, e.g. Camponotus Myrmicinae, e.g. Pheidole Solenopsis	Formicinae, e.g. Formica Myrmicinae, e.g. Myrmica	
Formicinae, e.g. Camponotus Myrmicinae Harvesting Ants Long-legged Dolichoderinae and Formicinae: in deserts	Myrmicinae, e.g. Tetramorium Formicinae, e.g. Formica Dolichoderinae, e.g. Tapinoma	
Some Dolichoderinae Some Formicinae, e.g. Colobopsis Oecophylla	Acanthomyops brunneus	
Ponerinae Myrmicinae Formicinae	Formica sp. Acanthomyops fuliginosis Myrmicinae Ponerinae	
Monomorium pharaonis	Monomorium pharaonis Prenolepis Iridomyrmex humilis Pheidole megacephala	
Solenopsis geminata Iridomyrmex humilis Pheidole megacephala Prenolepis sp. Odontomachus haematodes	Iridomyrmex humilis	
Crematogaster Monomorium Myrmica Pheidole Aphaenogaster Tetramorium Leptothorax (Myrmicinae)	Tapinoma Dolichoderus Myrmica Leptogenys Euponera Bothropmera Paltothyreus (Ponerinae)	Eciton } Dorylus } Dorylinae Pseudomyrminae Pachysima

Common Red Ants (*Myrmica rubra*) will need about a fifth of a teaspoonful of honey and a single squashed centipede (or other small insect) each week.

The illnesses of ants are legion. Many are incurable, but an immediate cleaning of the nest and the removal of the dead, and as many of the sick as possible, often yields good results. Sick workers can often be saved by being washed in a very weak solution of disinfectant of the non-carbolic sort and then placed in a clean nest. Painting of individual workers with a 50 per cent solution of alcohol with a soft paintbrush is often successful in combating mould. It also helps to remove mites, though this usually requires a long and tedious process of individual removal, each mite being picked off with a pointed knife or with forceps while the ant is held tightly between thumb and forefinger. Mites are clearly visible when present. There is no need to worry as to whether your ants are suffering from them; you will know when they are.

Experimental apparatus is more complex and each different apparatus needs a separate description. This is a matter for the specialist and he, like everyone else, must first learn to keep his ants successfully and to obey the few general rules given here.

CHAPTER 8

The Jig-saw Ants of Ireland's Eye

*

BEFORE continuing with the main story by describing how ants build their nests, a short diversionary tale about the odd results of some ant collecting must be told.

In the days when Dun Laoghaire, formerly Kingstown, was only a fishing village, way back at the end of the eighteenth century, travellers to Dublin landed at the port of Howth, on the northern side of the Liffey Estuary. Entering the harbour, they had to pass a small island which lies immediately opposite the harbour mouth, about a mile and a half from the shore. Not unlike the Isle of Wight in both its shape and its position in relation to the harbour, this small island of 'Ireland's Eye' is the guardian of a most remarkable mystery. It is the home of large numbers of abnormal ants, part male and part female.

Ireland's Eye gained its name from its likeness on the map to an eyeball held within the socket of Howth Head. To-day it is uninhabited, but a small chapel near the shore facing Howth Harbour is a relic of its former occupation. It is a small island, only three-quarters of a mile long and about half a mile wide at its widest point. It is popularly supposed that it was a leper island during the Middle Ages and the presence of two leper windows in the small chapel does much to bear this out. To-day its only visitors are week-end trippers, boys collecting seagull eggs, and an occasional fisherman.

The ant monsters were first found in 1945, when no fewer than 100 of them were found in a single nest of the Elbowed Red Ant (*Myrmica scabrinodis*). Since then several score more monsters have been found not only on the island, but also on the headland of Howth. These monster ants are, in appearance, just like jig-saws or mosaics, being made up of small fragments of male tissue and small fragments of female tissue, all jumbled together. Such mosaic creatures are not unknown to science. If something goes wrong with the fertilized egg of any living creature, instead of dividing into two similar cells, it divides into two dissimilar ones. When this happens at the first division of the newly-fertilized egg, then a creature that is literally cleft in two results, one half being male and the other being female. Similar abnormalities in the divisions of cells are thought to be the cause of monsters such as these of Ireland's Eye. At some very early stage of the cell division of the egg, part or the whole of one of the inheritance-controlling rods called chromosomes is lost and the mosaic jig-saw-like creature results.

There have in fact been thirty-seven such monstrosities described among the ants, apart from those found on Ireland's Eye and Howth Headland. The first one was found in 1851 by a German scientist called Tischbein in a nest of the Blood Red Slave-makers (*Formica sanguinea*). In one hundred years only three dozen others had been found by ant students throughout the world until the young Irish chemist, Desmond Walls, stumbled on the Elbowed Red Ants' nest on Ireland's Eye, one summer's day in 1945.

The puzzle about these jig-saw ants of Ireland's Eye and its neighbouring headland is that there are so many of them. Nearly two hundred have now been discovered. They are, moreover, not confined to a single species, having also been found on the headland in nests of the Common Red Ant (*Myrmica rubra*), and in one instance in a large Black Ant's nest (*Formica fusca*). Yet it is very rare indeed to find a single living creature of this sort and all the previous thirty-seven jig-saw ants had been isolated individuals found widely scattered throughout the world. Previous to these finds, scientists had thought that such things could only happen singly – to isolated individuals. At first it was thought that the appearance of this large number of jig-saw ants in a single colony must be due to some inherent abnormality in one of the queen ants to the colony; that all her eggs must produce monster forms. The finding of jig-saw individuals in other nests of the Elbowed Red Ant showed that this was not the case. A later theory that it might be due to some inherited trait dating back to some common ancestor among the Elbowed Red Ants on either the island or the mainland, proved equally inadequate when jig-saw individuals were also found among the Common Red Ants. The ants of two different species could scarcely have a common ancestor that would not have been so far back along the pedigree as to produce similar events elsewhere. It seemed unlikely that different species would interbreed to yield the same result without producing other changes and an abundance of intermediate forms which do not exist on either headland or island. One other theory remained. It is known that atomic radiation can cause many upsets in the development of living creatures and is especially prone to cause abnormal forms, though not usually of this kind. The monsters caused by radiation are more like those of fairy stories with extra or misplaced limbs and other unpleasant curiosities. Investigation of the geology of the region lent some hope to this hypothesis, for radio-active minerals are quite often found near veins of lead, and a vein of lead is known to run below this region. The lead vein runs from Wicklow to a hill called Kattygolliger, then dips under the sea and reappears in Howth and Ireland's Eye. Experiments over several years have produced no evidence of such radio-active deposits. Soil and water have been tested with a Geiger counter. It has remained silent, giving no record of any radio-activity, and the other plants and animals show no similar abnormalities. The mystery remains.

Another type of monstrosity occurs in ants as in other animals. This is the intersex: the creature which is almost wholly of one sex but inclines towards another. Such intersexes are caused not by trouble at the fundamental level of cell division, but by disturbances in the balance of the glands which govern both sex activity and the developments of what are usually termed the secondary sexual characteristics – e.g. the hair of a man's face. The intersex begins its development as one sex; but later, owing to a change in physiological conditions, development shifts so that some and perhaps even all of the organs are according to the pattern of the opposite sex. The intersex ant may look a bit like a jig-saw ant, but the mosaic is less scattered and is usually, in ants, confined to the head. These intersexes are not nearly so rare as the real mosaic or jig-saw ants. The American ant student, Morton Wheeler, once found a colony of fungus-growing ants, *Acromyrmex octospinosus*, which contained forty-one individuals whose heads were in part like the heads of queens and in part like the heads of workers. Another American ant student, Weber, found a colony of the Myrmicine relative of *Cryptocerus*, *Cephalotes atratus*, which contained no fewer than 4,000 individual queens, each of whose heads had some male characteristics. These intersexes are of interest mainly to the specialist student of ant genetics, but the jig-saw ants of Howth and Ireland's Eye are a mystery whose solution will be of interest to all students of science.

CHAPTER 9

Ants as Craftsmen

*

ANTS like the *Myrmica scabrinodis* and *M. rubra* of Ireland's Eye and Howth Head build simple nests with few chambers and passages. Although it is true that *M. scabrinodis* occasionally builds a small mound over its nests, those of *M. rubra* usually consist of only two storeys and about half a dozen chambers in all. The ant craftsmen are found among the Social Ants whose large societies necessitate the building of complete structures. The architecture of the Social Ants is so diverse that it is difficult to know where to begin to tell the story. Each species may have many different ways of building its nest. The Erratic Ant (*Tapinoma erraticum*) may build its nest in over thirty different styles, the oddest of which was one found in 1937 on Silchester Common in Berkshire, where the solarium was three feet away from the nest proper in the branches of a gorse bush. The nest itself was in the soil at the foot of the gorse bush and a heap built over it would have obtained little sunlight; so instead of a heap the ants built a cigar-shaped solarium six inches long and two inches in diameter of dead gorse and heather petals around the fork of two branches of the gorse bush. This is but one example of the adaptability of ant architecture. Each ants' nest is adapted to the particular locale in which it is built. There is no regular pattern that is used in only a slightly modified form in every circumstance, as is found in the nests of the bees and wasps. Many species of ants build nests of paper, although they are in a minority, but these carton nests are as variable in form and structure as the nests built in the earth. They may be within the hollow of a tree-trunk, hanging from a branch, between the axil of two branches, in the ground, or hanging in swathes between a branch and the trunk of a tree. They may have one entrance or many. The same species may construct one large nest two or three feet in length (all of carton), or half a dozen or even twenty smaller nests scattered throughout the tree. The same variability occurs in the species which do not make carton nests. The Occident Ant (*Pogonomyrmex occidentalis*) may build a single nest extending eight feet below the surface of the ground, or it may build a commune of ten or a dozen nests of lesser size spread over a territory four hundred yards square. The size of the nest is not necessarily related to the size of the ant. The Bearded Tree Ant, *Azteca barbifex*, a denizen of the vast flooded rain forests of the upper Amazons beyond Manaos, is only a tenth of an inch long, but its carton nests may be several feet long and one or two feet wide! Yet the giant *Dinoponera grandis* of the same region, which is over an inch and a half long, builds a simple nest in the earth some six inches across by a foot deep. Population, not size, is the controlling factor, and even in the ants whose colonies have immense populations there still remains the choice between the construction of one vast nest and many smaller ones. Some ants, like the Black Lawn Ant, *Acanthomyops niger*, of Europe, may build nests with or without hillocks according to the circumstances of the territory, while others like the Wood Ants, *Formica rufa*, always build some form of hillock. Sometimes it is very difficult to see any relationship between circumstance and the architecture of the nest, the form of the nest seeming to be more as if it were due to a whim than to any more casual explanation.

In the social ants, and especially in the *Formicinae* and *Dolichoderinae*, closely-related species will often be found making radically different types of nests. The tree-living *Azteca* of the South American forests may build its nest in the form of stalactite-like swathes, like *A. barbifex*; or it may build nests that are cylindrical or egg-shaped, like *A. aurita*; or it may attach the edges of leaves to the tree trunk and live underneath the shelter thus contrived, like *A. hypophylla*; or it may build a peculiar nest on the surface of flat stones on the forest floor, consisting of a host of meandering galleries, like *A. xysticola*. Other species of *Azteca* live inside the cavities of plants. The variety is almost endless. The Asian genus *Polyrhachis*, the spiny tree ants of the East, contains some species which make nests of carton, and others which make nests of silk. Yet other species of the same genus make their nests almost entirely of earth. The silk of the *Polyrhachis*, like that of some of the *Camponotus* (which mammoth genus also contains carton nest-makers, and species which make simple nests in the earth) and that of the *Oecophylla* is produced by the larvae, which, as will be seen, are used as shuttles in the nest-building process.

To attempt any hard-and-fast classification of the nests of ants is dangerous, for it would be found that the relationship between nest architecture and the ordinary classification and behaviour of the ant species is not an orderly one. In general the types of architecture employed by the ants can be listed as follows:—

1. Ants' nests constructed entirely in the earth and having no mound. Included here also are nests in felled and rotting wood.

2. Ants' nests constructed in the earth and having a mound.

3. Ants' nests constructed inside nuts, galls, or other such clearly defined objects.

4. Ants' nests burrowed out inside the solid wood of trees or inside the stems of living plants.

5. Nests made with carton.

6. Nests made with silk.

7. Nests within the nest of other ants.

8. Nests within human habitations.

The first group in the list contains the most primitive forms of ant architecture, forms which have evolved directly from the simple single-chambered room of the newly-fertilized queen ants. The nests, excavated in the virgin soil, are often underneath a stone. Directly beneath the stone will be found a series of two or three large chambers joined by passages. From the corner of two of these, dark funnel-shaped passages lead downward to the floor below. In summer-time the brood and queens will often be found within these upper chambers, but as soon as the colder weather appears they are removed as far below as possible. In its simplest form the earthen excavated nest has only one lower storey consisting either of a single large chamber, perhaps the size of a fob-watch, or two or three such chambers like the floor above. Such nests are those of the simple Ponerines and some *Myrmica* and other Myrmicines.

The temporary burrows of the Doryline Army Ants, who bundle *en masse* within a large simple hollow chamber in the earth, may be regarded as similar.

In their most complex form these earthen nests are as complex as any ant citadels. A large nest of the Ruddy Black Ant, *Formica rufibarbis*, may contain fifty or sixty such chambers. The nest of this ant is always connected with the surface by a single long passage. This is the only entrance to the city below. The city itself does not begin nearer than a foot from the surface of the soil and may extend for a depth of two or three feet further down. These nests, while the smaller ones of the same type are permanent habitations, occupied year in, year out, for many years, are rarely occupied for more than two seasons, whereas the nests of *Myrmica, Formica fusca*, and other ants, whose homes have few chambers, are often changed several times each year.

Such large-scale mining activities as those involved in a nest of fifty or sixty chambers usually necessitate the piling up of earth above the surface of the excavated area. How the Ruddy Black Ant avoids doing this is a mystery, for most large-scale excavators cannot.

There is then a large group of ants like the *Pogonomyrmex occidentalis* already mentioned who build their cities mainly below the ground, but form the earth which they excavate and bring to the surface into a relatively small crater-like dome. Many species of the Formicine genera *Acanthomyops, Prenolepis*, and *Camponotus*, the Myrmicine *Monomorium, Solenopsis, Pheidole*, and *Pogonomyrmex*, and the Dolichoderine *Dorymyrmex*, make nests of this type. The hillock above the nest is composed of the soil below with but few additions from the materials on the surface. Often, for this reason, it will be different in colour, as sub-soil and surface soil vary. The crater shape is due to the manner of its formation, the excavated soil being placed around the nest entrance which at first is itself kept clear. Then as the crater becomes larger the need for raising the entrance itself forces the ants to build around it. Usually in fact they abandon the original central entrance and re-shape the circular crater to make a horseshoe form with one or more entrances on its southern side. The crater hillock itself is excavated in order to provide summer chambers. The largest of such nests may contain over 4,000 chambers – perhaps many more, for they are difficult to excavate without damaging the structure.

The natural development from such a type of architecture is the hill architecture, in which either the earth excavated forms only a small part of the structure of the mound, or else the earth is excavated in order to form a mound for occupation rather than to dig out chambers below. These types, with the crater nests, form the second category in the list. They are best typified by the Wood Ants (*Formica rufa* and *F. exsecta*) on the one hand and the Yellow Hill Ant (*Acanthomyops flavus*) on the other. The Wood Ants collect the greater part of the materials for their huge mounds from the surrounding countryside. If the woodland trees are pines, then they collect pine needles; if they are oaks or evergreens, then they collect twigs and other debris. When kept in captivity they will build their hills of whatever material is provided, even doing their best to utilize glass beads! The size of their hills may be immense, reaching heights of seven to eight feet and a diameter of thirty to thirty-five feet. And, as has already been described (p. 72), this is but a part of the city, for excavations extend for many feet below the surface.

The Yellow Hill Ants build the common ant-hills of the European meadowland and mountain pastures. Rarely more than a foot in height, and usually lower, they are shaped more like sloping slag-heaps than the conical hills of other ants. The inhabited part of the hillock is the summit with the steepest slope. This summit nearly always faces south-east, to catch the rays of the morning sun, the longer slope of the hill tacking off to the north-west. This larger slope is the result of progressive building and abandonment of new parts as the colony grows. The peculiar shape of the nests of this ant and the constancy of its direction when left undisturbed has caused it to be used as a convenient compass guide by mountaineers who are caught in fog or have lost their way. It is easy to tell if the nests of these ants are occupied by pressing the surface of the hillock. If it gives way and feels soft and spongy, the hillock is occupied. If it feels hard and unyielding, then the nest is an abandoned one. In the meadows the Yellow Hill Ant often makes use of the earth cast up by the moles to start its building operations, and many a 'mole-hill' is more truly an ant-heap. Often its colonies occur in vast numbers, each nest quite separate from the others, but placed very close together. On the side of one slope of Thorpe Cloud in Dovedale, Derbyshire, there are over a thousand colonies within a very small area, giving the hill a pock-marked appearance when seen from a distance. Frequently the lower slopes of the Yellow Ants' nests are occupied by a colony of the Common Red Ant (*Myrmica rubra*), who find it a convenient already prepared nesting site and one from which they can make occasional stealing raids on their close neighbours.

These Yellow Ants demonstrate a point about ant habitations in general that may be little realized. The soil in the nest is very acid – much more so than the surrounding land – because of the presence of the ants. When, as often happened in the 1939–45 war, they were ploughed in, this acidity was spread over the field and affected the quality of the soil. It may improve it or it may harm it. There is no doubt that this is an important factor in soil chemistry in many districts and one which is usually not known. Indeed, a famous French law case in the eighteenth century concerned this very point, it being said that an area of several square miles of farm land had been ruined by the nesting of these ants.

A large number of ants make their nests inside nuts and galls. The small Myrmicine Ant *Stenamma* is nearly always found nesting in oak-galls, and the European Moss Ant (*Leptothorax tuberum*), although more usually, as its name implies, an inhabitant of clumps of moss, was once found nesting in a beechnut. Colonies of ants which nest in such small objects are, of course, small colonies of small ants. They rarely have a population of more than 100, or at most 200 individuals. Some species of the Janitor Ants (*Camponotus*, sub-genus *Colobopsis*), live inside oak-galls in Northern America. The doorway to their nest has but a single entrance which is round and is blocked and guarded by one of the janitor soldiers. All species of Janitor ants live inside some definite object through which they can cut out a circular doorway of appropriate size. They may live inside hollow twigs, or bamboo canes, anything which is or can be hollowed out, and which has a hard outer husk. The Swiss ant student, Forel, found the small Pseudomyrmine ant *Pseudomyrma gracilis* living inside the stems of dry grass in the Colombian savannah. The Common Guest Ant of Europe, *Leptothorax acervorum*, when it nests apart from its hosts, is frequently found inside old, dry, hollow twigs. The nests of *Azteca* and *Pseudomyrma* in *Acacia* thorns and in *Triplaris* have already been described.

It is in cases such as these that such lists of categories of ants nests fall down, for here is group 3 of the list merging into group 4. The wood-carving ants are, however, more distinct. The chief offenders are a group of *Camponotus*, the best known of which is *C. herculeanus* of the Eastern United States of America. Finding a weak spot in the bark, or the surface of a beam, this destructive Carpenter Ant bores inside and builds a regular warren of galleries. Even the largest and toughest of the forest trees are not proof against their onslaught, and they cause much havoc by their boring, trees, and sometimes beams and houses, collapsing as a result. Some of the *Colobopsis* janitor ants will bore into tough living wood in this way, but more usually they prefer a softer task for their nest-making. One ant in Europe is, however, carpenter-minded; this is the Brown Ant (*Acanthomyops brunneus*). The Brown Ant is a close cousin of the Black Lawn Ant and the Yellow Lawn Ant (*A. niger* and *A. umbratus*), but its habits are quite different. It lives solely in trees, high up on the branches. Widespread throughout Europe, Southern Asia (even as far south as Persia and Palestine), and Japan, it has an odd history in Britain. One hundred and fifty years ago it was apparently very common throughout Southern Britain, but by the end of the nineteenth century it was thought to have entirely disappeared from the British Isles. But in 1923 a single colony was found at Theale in Berkshire, and careful search showed that it was present in Windsor Forest also. Now it is a common ant in Windsor Forest, spreading outwards to nearby woods, and has also been found near Wokingham and the grounds of Wellington College. It is a very timid ant and lives a troglodyte existence on the trees, keeping plant lice of the genus *Stomaphis* under the bark.

Something of the diversity of the carton nests made by ants has been indicated in the earlier part of this chapter. They may be small or large; in the earth or up or within a tree. The largest carton nest on record is one large enough to contain a man; it was made by *Crematogaster schencki* in Madagascar. One of the smallest is that of *Camponotus* (*Myrmosphincta*) *folicola* of Trinidad, which makes a small rounded carton nest with only a single entrance and containing only a single chamber.

The majority of the carton nests of ants are suspended nests which hang from the branches of trees, like those of *Crematogaster* and most species of *Azteca* and *Dolichoderus*, but others, like those of the European *Liometopum*, may be inside the hollow trunks of trees, and some ants, like the Jet Black Ant (*Acanthomyops fuliginosus*), will build carton nests in the ground. The type of carton which ants manufacture varies greatly. That of the Jet Black Ant is largely composed of extraneous materials, usually of particles of rotting wood or failing this, of soil or grains of sand, stuck together with salivary material. When it is made of wood, the carton of these ants is covered with a black velvety fungus called *Lepto-sporium myrmecophilum*, which is only found on the carton of the Jet Black Ants. In the majority of carton building ants the material is purer, although it always contains a large amount of wood or soil. The ability to make these carton nests seems to depend on the degree of development of the mandibular glands. These glands provide the sticky, almost resinous substances which enable all species of ants to stick together the earth grains which form the bricks of their buildings. Even in species where the nest is entirely exca-vated and not built up, the passages and walls of the cham-bers are carefully lined with cemented earth. They are never left ragged and unbound.

It is this cement which makes it possible for the ants to build earthen aphid cowsheds for their herds in the stems and leaves of plants and bushes. In many of the commune-forming ants, the nests are connected by earthen-covered runways. A few species of Army Ants, which dislike the light, construct long tunnels as they march along, keeping always within them, yet building at such a pace that their march remains unhindered.

In the forests of Brazil the *Camponotus femoratus* and *Azteca ulei* (named after Ule, who discovered these nests) build hanging nests of earth in which the seeds of plants germinate and grow to form suspended gardens. The nests of the commune-forming *Azteca*, *Dolichoderus*, and *Crematogaster* of the tropics are nearly always joined by carton-covered passageways, and between the nests small subsidiary nests are built, forming temporary gathering-places for the wan-dering herdsmen and foragers. Often the ants will remain in these succursals over night to avoid the long journey back to their home. They enable the ants to maintain both herds and territorial domination over places at a considerable distance from their nests.

To watch the ants at work on their nests, whether they be of earth or carton, is a remarkable experience. McCook, in his book on Ant Communities, written nearly fifty years ago, gives a vivid description of the quiet excitement, care, and method involved. Having destroyed a part of a nest of the North American *Formica exetoides*, he watched the ants repair the havoc he had made: 'The work progressed by continuously adding earth pellets to the outer edges and pressing them into place. As the sides (of a destroyed gallery) rose they were gradually arched, and the springing of the arch was plainly seen. The curved edges approached in irregular lines, and at various spots the two projecting points drew nearer and nearer until they almost touched. It was quite exciting now to watch the delicate manipulation of the masons. Here came a worker with a pellet of a larger size than usual. She climbed the arch, moving more daintily as the top was reached. Holding on the while with her hind feet, she stretched across the wee chasm and dropped the ball of soil into the breach. The bridge was laid!

'And now, with surprising rapidity, it widened as the roof of the arch was covered. Until this was done, openings were left through which the ants moved back and forth, and which were closed over as sections of the arch were completed. They were temporary arrangements – "manholes", so to speak – for the convenience of the builders. Through these one could see the ants at work upon the inner surface, smoothing it with their jaws, as a mason would work with his trowel and mortar. The outside of the galleries and rooms was left rough, as laid, but the interior was smoothed.' Passages are arched and galleries are supported by pillars, each bit is carefully placed to support the next. No false passages are built which have no function, but deep down in the nest the drainage channels are just as carefully laid to end in blank walls of earth.

In temperate climates, the easiest ant to watch at work is the wood ant, thatching the top of her large dome. Each spring the thatch is built anew, but if it is too late to see this natural process a slight disturbance of the outer crust will, after the alarm has died down, bring an immediate commencement of repairs. Twigs of all shapes and sizes are pulled into place, laid lattice-wise beside and across one another. Next these larger beams are wedged tightly into place at either end. Then the smaller fragments are tightly drawn between until a solid mat is formed. When finished, this roofing is fully waterproof. On a wet day the material below it will be found to be perfectly dry. It is so tightly woven together that large chunks of it, often an inch or more thick and several inches across, can be removed without its falling to pieces.

The silk weaving ants use tools to make their nests. It is true that these tools are living and ready fashioned, but the behaviour of the weaving ants is none the less remarkable for that. All the weaving ants belong to the *Formicinae*. The habit is confined to the three genera *Camponotus*, *Polyrhachis*, and *Oecophylla*. The latter genus is the most famous for its weaving activities. One of its species, the Green Tree Ant, *O. viriscens*, was first discovered by Sir Joseph Banks during his voyage to Australia with Captain Cook. On 23 May, 1770, the *Endeavour* was anchored in Bustard Bay and Banks went ashore. On returning to his ship he recorded in his diary that 'upon the sides of the lagoons grew mangrove trees, in the branches of which were many nests of ants, of which one sort was quite green. These, when the branches were disturbed, came out in large numbers, and revenged themselves very sufficiently upon their disturbers, biting more sharply than any I have felt in Europe.' Later on he described the habits of these green ants more fully: 'green as a leaf, and living upon trees, where it built a nest, in size between that of a man's head and his fist, by bending the leaves together, and glueing them with a whiteish papery substance which held them firmly together. In doing this their management was most curious; they bend down four leaves broader than a man's hand, and place them in such a direction as they choose. This requires a much larger force than these animals seem capable of; many thousands indeed are employed in the joint work. I have seen as many as could stand by one another, holding down such a leaf, each drawing down with all his might, while others were employed to fasten the glue. How they had bent it down I had not the opportunity of seeing, but that it was bent down by main strength I easily proved by disturbing a part of them, on which the leaf, bursting from the rest, returned to its natural situation, and I had an opportunity of testing with my finger the strength that these little animals must have used to get it down. But, industrious as they are, their courage, if possible, exceeds their industry; if we accidentally shook the branches on which such a nest was hung, thousands would immediately throw themselves down, many of which, falling upon us, made us sensible of their stings and revengeful dispositions . . .'

These ants, being Formicines, do not in fact have stings, but wound their enemies by biting and then turn their gasters upwards over their backs and squirt acid into the wound. What Sir Joseph Banks had thought to be cotton was in fact silk, and it was not until 120 years later that the most astonishing part of these ants' behaviour was fully discovered. In that year an entomologist named Ridley observed *Oecophylla* workers holding grubs in their jaws and moving them to and fro inside the surfaces of two leaves held together in the fashion so well described by Banks. On looking closer, he found that a small silken thread issued forth from the mouth of each grub so employed and that the workers were in fact using their larvae as shuttles, weaving them backwards and forwards across the gap between the leaves and fastening the thread on one side or the other at the end of each movement. These marvels have since been confirmed by numerous other students. As the woven threads become strong enough to hold the leaves themselves, the main body of ants gradually release their hold and start to bend another leaf in place. They do this by forming a living chain across the gap from leaf tip to the spot at which it must be fixed. One ant climbs to the edge of the leaf and clings with its mandibles, another climbs over it and clings by its mandibles to the first ant's petiole (waist) and a third and fourth follow suit until the living chain is formed across the gap. The pulling process begins, the last ant pulling backwards with all its force and being joined by others who come to aid it with their strength.

Several such chains may be formed before the leaves are drawn close enough together for the sewing process to begin. While the weaving is in process the close-packed ranks of workers holding the two leaves together look just like so many stitches spread out along the length of the join.

The genus *Oecophylla* found in India, Ceylon, and Africa, as well as many species of the Spiny *Polyrhachis* of Asia and the Malay Archipelago, also weave nests. Some of these are made entirely of silk. Most of these pure silk nests consist only of a single chamber, or at most half a dozen, but Forel describes a remarkably superior edifice woven by one of the *Camponotus* weaving ants belonging to the sub-genus *Myrmobrachys. M. senex*, of South America, wove this nest in a triangular shape. It was about 8 inches high, 4 inches thick, and 5 inches across the base, and was perched on a twig, between its leaves. Inside were a multitude of small chambers two-fifths of an inch broad by one-fifth of an inch in height. These chambers were connected one to another by a myriad small columns and walls, all of which, like the chambers themselves, were made of pure silk woven from the larvae. The fineness of the work can be judged from the fact that, although exceedingly light, it was quite firm and of a tight texture.

Some of the nests of *Polyrhachis* are made of a mixture of silk and carton, some of silk and bits of debris or dry leaves (these are the so-called cotton nests), all woven together, but none can compare with this *pièce de résistance* of ant craftsmanship made by *C. senex*.

The two remaining categories of ants' nests in our list are not very different in character from those hitherto described. The nests of guest ants and of thief ants necessarily have one special character which differs from those of their hosts: they must be inaccessible. For this reason they are citadels of minute passages within a larger citadel. The guest ants, *Leptothorax* and *Formicoxenus*, are usually sculptured in the wood of the stump around which their Wood Ant hosts build their nests. Their colonies are small and they need little space and are accepted as friends by their larger hosts.

It is different with the thief ant, *Solenopsis fugax*, which also lives in the nest of the Wood Ants and other *Formicas*. Much smaller than *Leptothorax* and *Formicoxenus*, it builds its nests within the very walls of the galleries of ants it plunders, rushing forth to steal food and then retreating hastily within the minute passages before the larger ants can catch it. Its colonies are large and may number more than 100,000, and its depredations can cause serious loss to the ants whose citadels it invades.

Ants' nests in human houses or in ships or planes are much like mouse runs – in inaccessible places, between floors, within the walls, or among the foundations. Underneath a concrete or stone slab floor in a nice warm kitchen is a favourite place in houses. In ships they are most often found between the walls of cabins or between the inner platings of the hold. In planes they will nest around the heating pipes. Wherever there is warmth and protection and food close to hand, there the ants nest. Their nests in our habitations may not have the power to fascinate us like some of those out of doors which cause us less inconvenience, but they certainly show to the full the ability of the ants to adapt their nesting habits and architecture to the most diverse surroundings.

CHAPTER 10

The Ant World

*

THE time has come to enter the dangerous realms of ant psychology, to try to draw a rounder and perhaps more definite picture of the mental world in which they live. The adaptability of some ants is remarkable. The dullness, obtuseness, and seeming unchangeableness of the behaviour of other ants is, in comparison, equally astonishing. This variability can be seen even within the limits of a single colony. A Chinese scientist by name of Chen studied the different capabilities of different workers in a colony of *Camponotus*. The particular species he studied builds its nest in the ground. All of the workers in each colony were capable of digging a nest on their own, but the rate at which they worked differed. Some individuals worked more slowly than others. Some were just bone lazy and did scarcely any work when left to fend for themselves, while others beavered away at a great pace, like a dog searching for a buried bone.

If some of the energetic workers were put together, they got rather more work done than when they were left on their own, and if a less capable individual ant was placed with a more energetic one, then it worked the better for the stimulus of example. When the same individual was placed in the company of a lazy ant instead of an energetic one, then its work suffered, although that of the lazy ant was improved. If an energetic ant and a lazy ant were set to work together, then the poor lazybones really had to do some work – at least, he certainly set to with a better will.

The difference between the learning abilities of individual ants has already been discussed. Ants can learn mazes with six choice situations, or false turnings. A few can even learn mazes with ten false turnings. But maze-learning is not a good guide to the overall testing of learning ability, although in fact it is nearly always found that a good maze-solver is also better at learning the various jobs of work in the colony than its nest mates. The learning of jobs plays an important part in the life of every ant, but it should not be confused with intelligence, nor should its occurrence blind one to a realization that the basic factor underlying the doing of the jobs is instinctive. An ant may have to learn how to do a certain job in a certain situation, but it knows instinctively how to do the job. This sounds nonsense, but it isn't. Another statement of it runs like this: An ant knows instinctively that it must go outside the nest and get food when it is hungry (ignoring for the moment the fact that it also knows instinctively that it can get food by soliciting a returning forager); it knows instinctively how to milk aphid and coccid 'cows'; it knows instinctively how to suck the juices of a dead or dying insect. What it doesn't know instinctively is where to go and forage. Neither can it get back to the nest when placed far away from it in a region where there are no regular trails, although if it had gone to the same spot on its own volition, then it would, by means of memorizing its own compass reactions, be able to return. Memory, which means learning, also plays a part in captive ants – they learn by habituation, or repeated association, to accept their human captor. They become tame and cease to struggle when handled. After long periods of captivity ants will cease to try to escape even when they could easily do so, and wild ants will learn to come to a certain spot each morning, afternoon, or dusk (when foraging would normally have almost ceased) in order to collect food regularly placed out for them.

The part played by memory lasting over the winter and into the new year has been seen to be a most important factor in the re-establishment of the foraging trails, and in the commune-forming ants, the re-establishment of the links joining the individual colonies of which the commune is composed (see p. 73). The memory of the nest odours of the neighbouring colonies and also of the different species encountered on the foraging trails is also important during the spring awakening. This ability to remember is what makes the survival of the ants for more than a year so important a factor in their success. At the same time, the remarkable behaviour of *Oecophylla* and *Camponotus senex* in weaving the nest involves no learning ability nor intelligence *per se*. It is not a job which has to be learnt, although there may be things which ants can and do learn in relation to it. The whole job of building a *Camponotus senex* nest can be performed by *C. senex* workers without any learning being involved. The activity of nest building, even a citadel so complex as this, is guided throughout by instinctive knowledge. It is the result of behaviour that is inherited and which is not basically changed by the learning process.

Again, the functioning of the excitement centre ants (p. 60) reflects, but does not entirely depend on, learning. Its primary element is nothing to do with learning, being the ability of one ant to respond, to have its own instinctive desires aroused, by another ant which is performing an innate fundamental activity like tending the grubs, or setting out to forage. Its causal origin is probably linked with a variation in the metabolic rate (the rate and efficiency of food absorption and utilization) among the ants of the colony. Individuals having more efficient bodies will in fact work quicker and better. This factor may in turn be linked with a better brain structure, for a more efficient adult body implies the likelihood of a more efficient larval one, and a more efficient body during the period in which the brain is growing might be expected to lead to the development of a better and perhaps even a larger brain structure. We do not know whether in fact there is any relationship of this sort, but it seems highly probable. Certainly the difference in the development of the brains of the workers and queens, and of the non-working males, is striking. A more efficient body mechanism, too, would lead to a more efficient nervous system, whether or not there were any extra structural differentiation. Equally certainly the excitement centre ants do, as experiments show, have a greater ability to learn than the majority of the individuals in the community.

The extent and the limitations of this ability to learn are difficult to determine. The ability to learn and to remember is a quality which is a fundamental necessity for the economic success of the ant community, but it is probable that, by and large, the capacity to remember is a more important factor. A well developed memory is more important to the ants than a specially highly developed capacity to learn. A capacity to learn a large number of not very astonishing things and to remember them, coupled with extreme sensitivity of reaction to one another's behaviour, is the vital necessity for the successful working of the ant colony. Moreover, this learning and memory can be spread over a comparatively large number of individuals – the excitement-centre job-starters – providing the emphatic sensitivity to one another's reactions is well developed.

There are many tales that seem to make the behaviour of the ants reflect an ability to reason. Frequent instances of ants covering the sticky band on a tree with pieces of earth in order to gain a safe passage have been recorded. One of the first of these was described to Réaumur by the dreaded Cardinal de Fleury early in the eighteenth century. Other descriptions of ants finding food on a table whose legs were in spirit (to prevent their passage) and so climbing up to the ceiling, dropping thence on to the table, gathering the food and then dropping again to the floor, occur frequently in the early literature describing the behaviour of ants. Those ant students who have only studied ants in the laboratory and do not know their behaviour in the field, tend to regard the ants as stereotyped creatures capable of little learning. The ant students who have watched the ants under natural conditions over many years, as well as keeping them in captivity, are convinced that some element of reasoning is present in their behaviour.

Descriptions of events like those just cited add little to the argument one way or another. Ants will cover up a sticky or evil-smelling substance near their haunts whether or no it is of value to their foraging. Ants can indeed learn, and might learn to drop from ceiling to the table and then down again to the floor if it happened accidentally in the first instance. An even more remarkable feat of learning was accomplished by some *Myrmica punctiventris* and *Formica subsericea* under experimental conditions. The American scientist Turner succeeded in getting these ants to train themselves to drop from a platform with a pupa and carry it to the nest. Returning to below the platform, they then permitted Turner to replace them on the stage with a pair of tweezers, after which they repeated the act over and over again until all the pupae were safely removed into the nest. Further experiments by the same scientist showed a further remarkable ability to learn and utilize unusual events. He had been trying to teach two individual ants, 'A' and 'B', the way down from a platform to an island nest. This consisted of an inclined road. 'A' learnt the way quite easily and at once started to transfer the pupae to the nest, but 'B' proved obdurate ; with every encouragement of pushing and shoving, it refused to venture down the incline. Turner then, in despair, pushed a flat spatula underneath it and bodily transferred it to the island. When, having taken its pupa within the nest, it returned to the surface, he repeated the process in the reverse direction. After a few journeys the ant accepted this unusual mode of travel, stood perfectly still during the journey and crawled on to the spatula whenever it was presented to it. 'A' and her other companions, on the other hand, would have nothing to do with the spatula, rearing at it, attacking it, or avoiding it.

Behaviour of a different type can frequently be seen in the field when a colony of ants decides to emigrate, or when a new subsidiary colony is established in a *Formica rufa* commune. The author has seen several such mass movements in progress. On Meyrick Park Golf Links, near Bournemouth, on 17 September, 1939, a long line of Wood Ant workers stretched up the hill beside a railway cutting from a tree near the fairway. The majority of the workers were traveling down the hill to the tree ; each downward travelling ant carrying either a pupa or another worker ant. Beneath the tree a small nest, consisting of a hundred or so workers, was already established. Each ant on arrival plunged inside, and delivered its burden. Many were returning up the hill and over the top of the embankment to the mother colony, apparently in search of other workers and pupae. A close investigation showed, however, that many of the returning workers were those which had been carried to the new nest by other workers. Were they going back to fetch new allies or pupae, having learnt the way, or were they in disagreement with the policy of the move? Future observations on other colonies answered this question. In this case the move was completed over a period of ten days, by which time a fair-sized colony was established at the new site.

The start of such movements is a matter of disagreement. Some of the returning ants which had been carried down may have helped to bring down others – some undoubtedly would have done so – but many would not. They disagreed. At the beginning of such movements one or two workers, who have previously reconnoitred the spot, start to carry others to the new site. Often before they grip them by their thoraxes for porterage (when rightly gripped in this way all ants automatically relax) there is a sparring conflict. On arrival at the site, the ants who have been carried at once run back, together with the carriers. The instigators pick up more ants and the process is repeated, and because of the stimulus of their action they are joined by others. Eventually a plan is established. Unwilling workers still return to the old home, often carrying others with them, but then eventually get caught unawares by the impact of the influence of the activity of their original carriers and join the gang of outward travellers. Gradually the movement spreads. More and more ants join in. More stay at the new site than return, and soon get caught up by other stimuli and start to excavate and build. The conflict may even continue long after the establishment of the new colony. Some workers may refuse to move even after an old nest is virtually abandoned, living on in lethargic inactivity until their death.

Here, then, is another type of difference in behaviour between one ant and another. Whatever it is that adds the

force to the determination to move acquired by the instigators, is evidently of a complex character. It is the nearest
that the ants come to directive communication of the come-
here-do-this sort. Is there a grain of purpose here, or can it
all be explained away? Many scientists are apt to forget that
the so-called razor of the medieval philosopher William of
Occam cuts both ways. Occam said that no entity must be
assumed until it is necessary. The entities of all the complex
mechanisms of the no-reason-in-ants laboratory experimenters may just as well fall under the razor's swathe as the small
minute portion of reason or purpose that they refuse to allow.
They are certainly in danger of becoming over-complex,
because of their need to classify the whole of behaviour into
so many box-like compartments, flow between which can
only be obtained when an equally complex series of laws to
those used in defining the boxes are brought into play. The
fact is, it doesn't really matter if ants reason or not. Let
them, as Forel would have it, be 95 per cent instinct, 4 per
cent 'routine habits fairly rapidly acquired', and 1 per cent
reflection. Or let them be said to exhibit 'latent learning',
making use at one time of one part and another time of other
parts of a learnt pattern. What matter? Is reason such a
great gift, a sort of superior mantle, the possession of which
determines between the saints and sinners? The truth is
that there is no distinct line between learning ability of the
sort the ants show and reason. Discussing whether or not ants
reason is rather like discussing how many angels can sit on
the head of a pin.

What is important to know is the degree to which it is
permissible to think of ant behaviour in human terms. The
answer is simple – not at all. There is purpose in ant behaviour, purpose that, as Wheeler says, can scarcely remain
unappreciated by anyone who chances to sit on one of their
nests while picnicking. But there is no reason to make this
purposiveness all high falutin and full of thoughtfulness
and morals. It takes a great deal of thought to make a deep
reflection and it is certain the ants do not possess that
amount of ability. The whole of their social organization

can, as we have seen, be quite adequately described in the simplest terms, with a modicum of learning ability added to give good measure and success. Let us be content with that: they are.

One element of ant behaviour deserves a great deal more study than it has yet been given. This is the response reactions between the ants of the same colony – the empathy of the citadel. Inactive ants don't show it to the same degree. It breaks down in the queenless colony unless a quick replacement is made; never entirely, but to a large degree. How, anyway, is the response of worker-queendom (p. 30) elicited on one occasion yet not on another? Deprive a colony of their queens and reduce their numbers, and they become demoralized and lose the will to live. Beware experiments of queenless colonies: their behaviour is but a shadow of reality. Yet in nature more stamina is often found and workers lay eggs and new queens are sought at the marriage flight. Sometimes, as in the case of the Wood Ants staying, queenless, in the old nest, this is not the case: they will not move: they would rather stay, linger on awhile and die, for that is their fate. In these problems we are reaching somewhat blindly, and with groping gestures, towards the core of the mystery of the ants. Well-being brings to them a finely-tuned response to antish things. The open extravert swayed to and fro by the slightest touch of stimulus or instinct or memory; the welling up of immense desires, upon the playing of the faintest chord that is a part of its patterned tune; the life at full stretch of nervous quiver until tired beyond response in any field. These are the characteristics of the ant world as near as can be put in human terms – and how abominable they are to the psychologists, for what could be more anti-social than the characters just described? Human analogies are not permissible in seriousness, and yet how odd! The key to the ant world is in their openness one to another, their tuning to the slightest tremor of response in others. Sometimes, as in the soldier ants of *Pheidole*, this takes a more palpable form. These monster-headed creatures wander slowly in and out and round the nest and up and down the trails until suddenly a change occurs. An alarm spreads excitement through the colony. The workers rush about with ever-increasing speed, until suddenly all together the ponderous soldiers come to life. They run with open jaws and snap at enemies supposed and real. Gone is their lethargy : gone their vagueness, full of purpose they rush to defend the colony. The alarm is over, the excitement dies, the movement slows and suddenly they are back in lethargy, not quite all at once as at the start, for individual unwinding is less equal than mass rousing. Just pure physical movement seemed to do it. It may be that nervous tension of excitement round about was the cause deeper down below inside the ants, but the outward sign was clear and physical enough.

The quick reaction of an ant to the work of its neighbours can bring great dangers. An individual ant whose sense of smell is destroyed and who is in pain can destroy the peace of a colony and start off a hundred battles to the death. This is the way in which sublimate scattered on the ants destroys them. A few individuals with their feelers covered with it and in pain from its chemical burning will set about all and sundry who come near them. Some of their colleagues will aid them, recognizing them correctly as members of their own colony. Other colleagues will help the individuals they have so wantonly attacked, equally correctly recognizing them as fellow members of the colony. The spirit of alarm and of fighting spreads. An object to fight, to bite, and poison is needed for the consummation of the train of action which has been triggered off. Here in the combatants is a source of satisfaction. A friend is helped to hold the creature she is fighting – what more natural? An ant which arrives in the middle of the two combatants is confused, will turn away, obviously puzzled. If, on the other hand, a tangled mass of fighters is already established, then she has something definite to do; she seizes hold of one of the legs of one of the outermost of the combatants and pulls. This is standard ant warfare practice. It is essential that an ant which is fighting should not lose its grip on the ground.

It must keep its balance and not permit itself to be dragged along or, above all, be overturned. However badly it is being hurt it must hang on with as many legs as are left to it in order to prevent this last disaster. For once overturned, its protective armour is of little value. Its less heavily-armoured belly and the ventral surface of its waist are exposed and it is unable to use its own weapons with any certain effect. Its long, spreadeagled legs are a hindrance to its righting itself, making the process difficult at the best of times, and almost impossible in the midst of a battle. The battles of individual ants are a type of desperate wrestling match, with weapons allowed and no holds spared; long periods of stillness, with each combatant holding the other fast by a ferocious grip, alternate with sudden movements of attempted change to obtain a better and more damaging grip. During the changes, stings, squirted acid, or vicious mandible bites will be attempted. Meanwhile the supporters of either side will hang on, often in chains three deep, to the legs of their favoured candidate and so prevent her being overthrown and landed at a disadvantage. Sometimes a third ant will join in the fight more definitely and attack its friends apparent, but unless there is a considerable difference in size between the combatants there is danger in this. It may be of little help to the colleague, disturbing her grip rather than aiding the battle. It is an odd thing that when the two combatants are evenly matched, such direct interference is usually, at least in the early stages of the battle, limited to an odd snap at an eye, or at the armour of the thorax or gaster. An eye so pierced bleeds, yielding a large quantity of colourless thick sticky blood, and the dents which can be made in the thorax and gaster by a well-placed bite need to be seen to be believed.

Where the species are of very different sizes, as for example in a battle between the Black Lawn Ant and the Wood Ant, several of the smaller species will attack each of the larger ants. The point that led to this diversion about the warring of ants is the importance of the group or colony mood to the individual and *vice versa*. It is a system of fluxion.

The emotive forces flow outwards from each individual to his neighbours and in the opposite direction at varying *tempi*. When excitement develops, each individual receives impulses at a greater rate and of greater intensity from all the surrounding individuals, and since they are being excited, moving rapidly to and fro, from more of them. As its own excitement mounts as the result of this vast inflow of tensions, so its own impulses flow outward at an ever-increasing rate, and its own more and more hurried movement brings it into contact with more and more individuals from whom and to whom it both receives and gives ever more tense and frequent stimuli. It is as though each of these stimuli toned up a spring inside each ant a little tighter, a spring which is always steadily running down while the ant is doing things and, granted no stimulus, runs down eventually to a standstill until some new stimulus from another ant, from an outside event, or from inside the ant's body through hunger or some other bodily want, causes a winding up again, making the ant tick once more. This is not meant to be anything more than a descriptive analogy. It has no actuality except for the picture of the fluctuating interactions of the ant community that it enables one to draw.

The ant state as a whole cannot (as has been suggested by some writers) be compared to the human body, with a corporate wholeness and a large number of individual organs, for each individual ant has an ability to learn and remember and to respond to situations differently. It has, moreover, an ability to do something off its own bat. It is not merely a responding machine, it is also very definitely a doing machine, firing off its energy in a positive manner whatever the stimuli around it may be. What it does is affected by the stimuli around it and inside it, but it does do the things of its own volition. It is guided in its actions by these stimuli, but it is not made to do things as a result of them. A sleeping ant will, if tired, sleep the sleep of the just and be d – d to heaven and hell let loose, unless the excitement reaches so great a nervous pitch that, like the soldiers of *Pheidole*, it cannot any longer remain lethargic and at rest. This flow of the nervous energy of ants throughout the community is a definite and little understood phenomenon. Nervous tension can be produced by the physical conditions of a thunderstorm, or rather of the tension prior to the actual storm. To a lesser degree the tension of extreme nervous excitement can be mounted by temperature, but never so fully as in the case of true psychologically-created tensions or those engendered by approaching storms. The metabolic rate is obviously a factor of importance in connexion with this tension phenomenon. As the ants have no mechanism of bodily temperature control, it might be argued that the ants, responding as they do directly to the change of temperature by an increased activity, are merely reflecting by their excitement a direct effect of temperature on their metabolism. There is some truth in this, but it is not the whole truth. Ants are much more excitable in hot weather. A rough approximation of ant activity to temperature could no doubt be made. In hot weather they move faster. In cold weather they move slowly. But once the temperature has increased above a certain minimal degree, and their foraging trails are extended, normal activities are established, and they may reach just as great a pitch of nervous tension on a thundery day in cool weather as in hot weather. Their tension when the alarm is sounded on a cool day is every whit as great as that on a hot one. Indeed, on the hottest day a measure of sleepiness often gains dominance during the midday heat. This rising and ebbing nervous tension in the ant community is something distinct from such general effects as those of hot and cold temperature on their metabolism. Once the colony activity is established – i.e once the ants are awake after their winter or their night's sleep – there is always a light tension throughout the colony. If the ant colony is regarded as a number of units spread throughout a certain area, it will be found that this tension varies throughout the area. There are localities of concentration where jobs are being undertaken, and localities of low tension where the current may be said to flow weakly. These are the areas where the ants are inactive.

In a sense this concept of the ant colony as a field of tension in which there is flow between the units and build-ups in some localities and drainage from others, is something like the theories evolved for the electrical mechanisms of the brain. Certainly ants do behave as a colony much like a conglomeration of nervous tissue. Nerve cells, like ants, exhibit considerable independence of action, while yet contributing to the behaviour of the neighbouring nerve cells and the nervous system as a whole, and receiving in return a series of more powerful influences, which are more powerful because of the dominance of the whole system over each individual unit. A nerve cell cannot survive on its own; it is tied by a bond to its neighbours. Yet it is free to migrate, to grow, degenerate, and regenerate again, more or less of its own accord, in dependence on local conditions and necessities. We know very little about the micro-physiology of the nerve cell as yet, but much work is in progress which may help to elucidate it. Practically no work has been done on the physiology of the ants, or the study of their metabolism or their nervous system, not even the physical aspects of it. When they are undertaken, the study of these aspects of ant life will yield the key to this fundamental mystery of their social organization of aggregates of living units as a whole, whether the units be nerve cells, animals, or even human beings. The excitement centre mechanism operates through this nervous tension which early in this book was called 'empathy', or 'sensitivity', or 'interaction'. The 'excitement centre' mechanism is the more superficial key to the organization of the ant community. It is just as important to the success of that organization, for without it the bond of nervous tension would lead nowhere in the field of positive action. But without this basic element of the nervous tension the excitement centre mechanism could not work. The excitement centre ants, the job-getters, have in fact to be retranslated at this stage of the formulation of the problem into units of high potential in the general field of nervous tension, which is spread out throughout the whole ant colony. It may well prove, in the light of future experimental work, more advisable to call them units of higher metabolic rate. For the moment 'excitement centre' or 'job starter' are safer terms because they describe behavioural functions. We do not know what physiological and nervous mechanisms control the behaviour of the ants, but we do know what the ants do. We can watch and describe the behaviour of the individual ants (and of the colony as a whole) and the interactions which are seen to take place between them, much as we describe their learning ability, or the learning ability of human beings, without actually knowing the mechanism of the brain.

It is time to draw the strings together and to begin to close the story before opening it again for a brief while in a new light, through the characters and work of those who have contributed most towards their study and therefore towards this tale. The ants are neither automatons, nor miracles of intelligence. They are not objects for moral lessons for either young or old. They can be both lazy and diligent. They can learn and may possess something akin to intelligence. They feel pain and would seem to exhibit anger, but not having the *entrée* into their minds, one cannot know that they experience any emotion. They have no language in the sense we understand it, but they copy one another's actions and responses to situations. Certain individuals seem to be of special economic importance to the community since they tend to be the ones who start off all the many activities of the division of labour in their complex societies. Yet they have no leaders who say 'come here and do this.' There are non-social ants and highly social ants with a vast number of intermediate types; but there is no comparable progression through stages of hunting, nomadism, and dairying, as in man. All these phenomena are found among the ants, but one should not draw human analogies. The mystery of the ants is in their empathy, the bond of nervous tension which builds so quick a response one to another that it seems more akin to a response to a nerve-carried impulse within a single individual than one involving two quite separate and recognizable characters separated by space. Analogies have been drawn to describe this phenomenon, but remember they do not explain it and are meant only to communicate the description of the event.

Lastly, remember the multitude of the ants, their vast numbers, their 15,000 species of divers form and habit, their numerous guests and camp followers, their ubiquity and dominance throughout the world. Do not forget that even if there are only 50,000 ants (the number in a moderate sized wood ant nest), to each acre of the forty million square miles of the warmer regions of the earth – a most moderate and undoubtedly inadequate estimate – there are to-day as you read this 1,280,000,000,000,000 ants crawling in and around the surface of the earth. The true figures is probably nearer 10,000,000,000,000,000. We know from experimental figures that these ants dig up large quantities of earth. Allowing for the fact that many live in trees and not in the earth, and that many are non-social, and in temperate regions reach but a fraction of the navvying capacity of the Brazilian Stakhanovites, an estimate of fifty tons of soil shifted per square mile of this two-thirds of the earth's surface gives the incredible weight of 200,000,000 tons per annum. Again, the real amount is probably much greater and nearer the figure of 8,000,000,000 tons of sub-soil moved each year. Furthermore, taking the lowest of the two estimates of numbers, the insects the ants eat each day would fill at least 320 million two-gallon petrol cans!

In the face of such facts as these, no one can question the important, if indirect, part the ants play in our economy and thereby in our lives. It is time that the importance of the study of them was more fully realized.

CHAPTER II

Some Famous Ant Men

*

THE breadth of the ant world is great enough to allow for many students and diverse enough to attract many different aspects of its study. It is a striking fact that the study of ants has never been directly financed. Only one student of these fascinating and, as it is hoped has been shown, important creatures has ever been able to settle down to a lifetime's work of ant study. This single exception was a professor of entomology at Harvard University, U.S.A. As one looks back through the scores of volumes of ant literature (there are forty-four within a hand's reach on the shelf as this is written), a great cavalcade of characters passes by. Many of the greatest of ant students are little known to science; some achieved fame in other fields. We owe Bank Holidays to one, modern methods of steel-making to another. One of the most famous of all was a Jesuit priest; another was a professor of psychiatry. The Church of England contributes two celebrated English students, and an engineer produced the first great manual of the ant's internal anatomy. A man about town of the Gay Nineties became England's greatest student, and until he died last year was the sole surviving member of the 'Great Five' of ant study. The Great Five were Auguste Forel of Switzerland (the Professor of Psychiatry), William Morton Wheeler of the United States of America (the Professor of Entomology at Harvard), Eric Wasmann of the Netherlands (the Jesuit priest), Carlo Emery of Italy, and Horace Donisthorpe of Great Britain (the Man about Town). These five revolutionized our knowledge of ants. They worked in the last decade of the nineteenth century and the first half of this century, producing in its first thirty years a flood of literature covering the habits, anatomy, and classification of the ants of the world. Each of these five great ant-men was inspired by earlier students. The history of ant-men extends a great deal farther back.

At the top of the tree, as the father of our present knowledge of the ants, must be placed René-Antoine Ferchault de Réaumur, the last great universal genius. Born at La Rochelle in France in 1683, during the reign of Louis XIV, *le roi soleil* and one of the greatest kings of France, he was a son of one of the Judges of Appeal of that city. It was he who discovered the modern methods of making steel. He also discovered how birds use their gizzards to grind their food, how turquoises are the teeth of dead mastodons, and invented the thermometer which bears his name. He even tried to find a commercial use for spider's silk. Réaumur left behind him, when he died, 138 portfolios of manuscripts, the chief of which were those of his *History of the Insects*, published in six volumes during the years 1734–42. One manuscript part of this work, the most important as far as the present story is concerned, remained unpublished for 182 years. This was his *Natural History of the Ants*. Although it was written in the years 1742-3, it was never published during his lifetime, and after his death was lost among a mass of papers in the Institut Français until its discovery in 1925 by Wheeler, and it was published in the following year.

In this work Réaumur scotches many of the stories of the ancients and gives a wonderfully clear outline of the behaviour of the ants he knew in France. He disbelieves Solomon's account of the ants' harvesting their grain, but so at that time and for a full century afterwards did all the European scientists. Réaumur was only interested in the ants' behaviour, of which he gives a fascinating outline, and he used the behaviour of the insects as the basis of their classification, with remarkably accurate results. It may be asked how Réaumur's work, so long hidden, could influence the ant students who worked between the time it was written and the time of its publication. The answer lies in the friendship of Charles Bonnet (1720-93), a young Swiss disciple of Réaumur's, with a blind student of bees, François Huber (1750-1831). François Huber knew of Réaumur's work on the ants from Bonnet; probably like another French scientist, Lyonet, he had seen at least a part of it. At any rate it was because of this work and that of Bonnet himself that François Huber encouraged his son Pierre to study the ants. Pierre needed little encouragement and in 1810, when he was thirty-three, he published the most famous of all books on ants, his *Researches into the Natural History of Indigenous Ants*. This book, translated ten years later into English by James Johnson, has been aptly called *The Bible of Myrmecology*.* Pierre Huber ends the introduction to his book with the following paragraph : 'The number of questions not yet solved is endless; it is, however, time to fill up some of the numerous sketches which our predecessors have left us upon this subject, and place, if possible, the history of ants on a more solid and secure foundation.' He succeeded. The foundation is as secure to-day as on the day his work was published. It was Huber who first described the slave-raids of the Amazon Ants (*Polyergus rufescens*) and the Blood Red Slave-making Ants (*Formica sanguinea*); it was he who first discovered the true facts of the marriage flight and the subsequent colony foundation; he first adequately described the relationship between the ants and their aphid cows; and he gave us the first true picture of the organization of the ant colony.

We know little about the life of Pierre Huber, save for one extraordinary fact that he was an 'old flame' of Auguste Forel's grandmother. It was this relationship that was the direct cause of Forel's studying the ants. Let him describe the incident for himself (introduction to his *The Social World of the Ants*, London, 1927): 'One memorable day my grandmother brought me Huber's *Recherches sur les mœurs des fourmis indigènes*, published in Geneva in 1810. The copy had been dedicated to her by the author. "There," she said, "I will make you a present of this book, written by my old flame Huber. He was not cruel like you, for he scolded me when I killed the ants that were eating my jam. I

---

* Myrmecology is, in my opinion, a quite unnecessary technical term, meaning Ant Study.

have never been able to get through his book. It isn't my style." '

Forel 'devoured' Huber's book and turned anew to watching the ants around the shores of Lake Geneva, where his parents lived. He published his first paper on ants while he was still a twenty-one-year-old medical student in 1869, and six years later published his own classic work on the ants, *Les Fourmis de la Suisse* (The Ants of Switzerland). It was not until he was an old man that his *Social World of the Ants* was published in five volumes. By the time the last was finished in 1923 he was seventy-five years old. He published nearly 500 papers on ants in scientific journals.

A wise, kindly man, he was an odd mixture of scientist and moralist. He helped to revolutionize our knowledge of the classification of ants, finding, describing, and naming hundreds of new species. But, as might be expected from a medical man specializing in neurology and psychiatry, he was especially interested in their physiology, their nervous structure, and, above all, in their behaviour. He had one fad which brought him many quarrels; he was an ardent Socialist and insisted that the ants taught us that peace could only be achieved through socialism. He quarrelled with Wheeler about the brain structure of the ants and with both Wheeler and Emery about their classification, for he was very obstinate and apt to be dogmatic. Donisthorpe, an equally ardent Tory of the old school, likewise quarrelled with him, as naturally did Wasmann, the Jesuit, whose approach to the study of ants' psychology left Forel, an ardent follower of Sémon, aghast. For all that he was a kindly man, as quick to forgive as to quarrel, and after all most of the others quarrelled amongst themselves in any case. This is a real hindrance to the understanding of the work of these five great men. They quarrelled as to whether the ants should be divided into five sub-families or into eight. Something of the confusion this created can be seen from their arbitrary handling of the two tribes, *Cylindromyrmicini* and *Acantho-stichini*.

Carlo Emery contributed the section on ants in the

Genera Insectorum, that master key to the world's insects. He placed both tribes in a section of the Ponerines which later became the *Cerapachyinae.* Wheeler disagreed and in 1922 placed the first one in with the Ponerines and the second one, like Emery, in the *Cerapachyinae.* Then in 1944 Donisthorpe completely reversed the process, placing the first one in with the Cerapachyines and the second one in with the Ponerines. What can the poor ordinary student do when this sort of thing is the order of the day, not only in the highly complex field of nomenclature of ants, but also in descriptions of their actual behaviour?

Time has ironed out much of this confusion, and the breadth of their work remains as a monument to their achievement. Carlo Emery spent a lifetime's work in between his other jobs at the Museum in Geneva in working out the classification of the ants – a thankless task for which he often got little but criticism and argument as a reward. Wheeler, the greatest of them all, was, like Forel, an all-round man. His greatest work, strangely, was his study of the ants of the Belgian Congo, though his textbook on the 'Ants' will, like Forel's *Social World of the Ants,* always remain one of the major compendia of ant lore. Like Forel, too, he wrote hundreds of scientific papers about the ants, but then so did all five. His most important contribution was to work out the mutual feeding relationship between the ants and their grubs and to understand the vital rôle it played, not only between the ants and their young, but between the adult ants themselves. He had a thorough knowledge of the classics and an appreciation of the finer things of life that coloured all his studies. A great friend of Donisthorpe's, he was of quite a different mould, belonging to the academic sphere of the common room rather than the *savoir faire* of the larger world. He was the only one of the five to leave a numerous body of students, many of whom unfortunately did not continue their studies for long after his death in 1937.

Donisthorpe must have a special niche in the Englishman's heart. He was a great character. Born into Society in the late Victorian days, he kept house in great style at Lancaster Gate for many years until misfortune hit him hard and he lost his fortune. Then he had to do his best to eke out his meagre income with what he could gain from his ant work, which, with no university degrees behind him, proved little enough. At first his knowledge of ants came to him mostly from expeditions in the field. He solved the problem of how the slave-makers and the temporary parasites founded their colonies. He was a great student of beetles also, and discovered much about the relationship between the ants and their guests. Later, as he became older, he took up the study of the classification of the ants, and shortly before he died he published the first complete skeleton outline of the classification of this group. As befits an ardent Tory, he always wore a buttonhole, and would never dream of venturing out to dine without carrying with him a bunch of flowers for his hostess. He was proud of the feats of his youth, in particular of his achievement, in his twenties, of swimming the Rhine near Heidelberg, a feat which, so it was said, no one had achieved before. He published a remarkable book on the British ants (1927) which contains within its covers a vast mass of relevant and irrelevant data that only he, with his mania for indexing and scrapbooks, could have compiled. His *Guests of the British Ants* (1928) is still, with Wasmann's *Ameisenmimikrie* (1925) the leading book on ant guests. Wasmann was the greatest of all students of the guests of ants, of which he described many hundreds. A Jesuit and a scholar, he brought the panache of the theologian philosopher to his book on the *Psychology of the Ants and of the Higher Animals* (1905). He shares with Forel the distinction of discovering the ant communes and of understanding their structure. His studies of the Blood Red Slave-making ant are unique in their detail and scope.

Three other names from the last century stand out as of a stature near to these five just mentioned – Santschi, lover of North Africa and the student of the ants of the deserts; Charles Janet, the French engineer whose studies of the internal structure of the Common Red Ant (*Myrmica rubra*) are still the basis of our understanding of ant physiology; and Ernst André, whose brother (like Huber's father) was a famous student of bees. Janet discovered that the queen ant lives on the fat developed from her wing muscles while she is founding her colony. Santschi made a series of classical studies on the manner in which ants find their way. André brought our knowledge of the relationship of the ants and the aphids a great step farther forward from the days of Huber's early studies. All three were French and all were inspired by Huber.

It was the British who discovered the Army Ants and the fungus-growing ants, and who rediscovered the Harvesting Ants. Bates, in his *The Naturalist on the Amazons* (1863), first described the behaviour of the Säuba leaf-cutting ants of tropical America, and his compatriot Belt first pierced the mystery of their nests and found that they grew mushrooms on the chewed-up mulch of the leaves they picked (*A Naturalist in Nicaragua*, 1874). The English missionary, the Rev. T. S. Savage, first described the marches of the Army Ants of Africa in a communication he made to the Entomological Society (now the Royal Entomological Society) in 1847. But it is only within the last few years that the studies of the American ant student, T. C. Schnierla (who was also the first person to experiment with ants in mazes), have elucidated the mechanism of the rhythm of their nomadism.

One of the greatest queries in the ant world of the last century concerned the veracity of Solomon. Did ants really harvest grain or not? There was no evidence that they did, but could the Bible be wrong? It was not. In May, 1869, Mr Bentham, to quote Traherne Moggeridge, 'in his presidential address to the Linnaean Society called attention to the want of reliable information as to the existence of such subterranean accumulations of seeds as are popularly supposed to account for the sudden appearance on railway cuttings, gravel from deep pits, and the like, of crops of weeds hitherto unknown in the district.' Moggeridge was present at the meeting and the question struck a chord. Might not the ants which he had seen carrying seeds at Mentone in the south of France be the unconscious agents responsible both for the distribution and the subterranean storing of seeds? Already a certain Dr Lincecum had given an account of the manner in which *Myrmica* (*Atta*) *barbata* (now *Pogonomyrmex barbatus* and no relative of either *Myrmica* or *Atta*) stored seeds of 'a particular rice-like grass' and even, so he said (wrongly as it turned out), maintained a crop of this grass around its nest. Moggeridge determined to find out and set out on 29 October, 1871, to find the valley where he had seen the grain-storing ants. He found the ants, a species of *Messor*, and proved that they did indeed store grain and fed on it. His studies were described two years later in his book on the *Harvesting Ants and Trapdoor Spiders*, London, 1873. Solomon was right, and so was Virgil and many another of the classical writers.

The Honey Ants of the Garden of the Gods (*Myrmecocystus*) were discovered by an American cleric of a military family, Henry C. McCook, D.D., in 1882 (*The Honey Ants and the Occident Ants*, published in London). He not only described the anatomy of the repletes and the manner in which their gasters were gradually distended, but he also cleared up the mystery of Dr Lincecum's Agricultural Ant. It was, he found, indeed a harvester, but the purity of the grass near its nest was not in fact always true, and in any case it was nothing to do with the ants – they did not cultivate the grain in the way we farm crops, though damp seeds thrown out might account for some of it.

One of the greatest of ant-men has still to be mentioned. The banker, Sir John Lubbock, the inventor of Bank Holidays, who later became Lord Avebury, was the father of the experimenters on ants. He tried to find out about their way-finding; he tried to study their powers of communication and their intelligence. In order to do this he devised and carried out long series of experiments. In many cases they were inconclusive, but he did manage to show that they had no language. He also discovered that ants see ultra-violet light. These studies, with full experimental details, will be found in his book, *Ants, Bees, and Wasps*, which was published in 1874.

Who else to mention? Rather who not to mention, the names come so thick and fast. The Rev. W. Gould, who in 1747 published the first British book on ants; Brun, the German, who made such elaborate studies about the orientation of the ants; De Geer, the Swiss, who first studied the fossil ants; the Rev. Farren White, who wrote that most charming book *Ants and Their Ways* (1895); Arnold, who wrote a monograph on the ants of South Africa; Swammerdam, Bondroit, Latrielle (co-mentor with Bonnet of Pierre Huber) and Schmidt. The names flow on. And what of the story-tellers like the Comtesse de Gence, who wrote a wonderfully accurate and fascinating tale about Gigi, the little boy whose shirt still hung out when he was turned into an ant for being lazy? Or Ferenczy, who pestered Donisthorpe for information about ants until he got it, and wrote a vivid satire of the human race in the *Ants of Timothy Thümmel* (1924), and then committed suicide in his disgust, leaving Donisthorpe and Evelyn Cheesman to fill some scores of pages about the realities of the ant life on which he had drawn?

It is perhaps invidious to mention living students, though one exception has been made already, but the names of Creighton, Mann, Marion Smith, and Weber in the U.S.A., and Escherich, Gösswald, and Stitz in Germany and Hölgersen in Norway, will in turn take their place in the roll of honour of ant history. And in Britain to-day a new generation of young ant-men is rising to follow in Donisthorpe's footsteps. There is much to be done, and throughout the world there are far too few at work on the study of these fascinating and important insects. Is it too much to hope that some of the readers of this book may join them and follow in the footsteps of these great ones of the past. If so, then its purpose will, at least in part, not have failed.

INDEX

185